John
with love
from Pamela

Jan 7ᵗʰ 1983.

THE
SHOTGUN

THE SHOTGUN

Macdonald Hastings

DAVID & CHARLES

Newton Abbot   London

British Library Cataloguing in Publication Data

Hastings, Macdonald
    The Shotgun.
    1. Shotguns—Great Britain—History
    I. Title
    683.4'26   TS536.8

ISBN 0-7153-8062-1

Typeset by ABM Typographics, Hull
and printed in Great Britain
by Butler & Tanner, Frome and London
for David & Charles (Publishers) Limited
Brunel House Newton Abbot Devon

Reproduced facsimile from the
Dedication to the Ninth Edition of
Instructions to Young Sportsmen in all that relates to
GUNS AND SHOOTING
by Peter Hawker – the 'father of gameshooting'

Dedication to the Ninth Edition.

TO

FIELD MARSHAL

HIS ROYAL HIGHNESS

THE PRINCE ALBERT

OF

SAXE-COBURG AND GOTHA,

K.G.   K.T.   K.P.   G.C.B.   G.C.M.G.

&c. &c. &c.

SIR,

THE gracious permission to dedicate this
edition to Your Royal Highness not only confers
on me the greatest honour that can be granted to
a British Sportsman; but also gives me the heartfelt
pleasure, before I leave the field, of inscribing my
humble production on Guns and Shooting to a
distinguished patron of the one, and a noble example
for the manly exercise of the other.

I have the honour to be,

SIR,

Your Royal Highness's ever dutiful

and obedient Servant,

PETER HAWKER.

DEDICATION

To HRH The Duke of Edinburgh
PRINCE PHILIP
who graciously permitted me to dedicate
this work to him in a tradition of royal
patronage dating from the time of
Colonel Peter Hawker, and one hundred
and fifty years after the development
of contemporary game gun shooting.

'I ranged o'er the fields from morn until night,
My dog and my gun my constant delight:
I traversed the coast and the fields void of care;
What pastime on earth can with shooting compare'

A doggerel by CAPTAIN LACY (1842)

CONTENTS

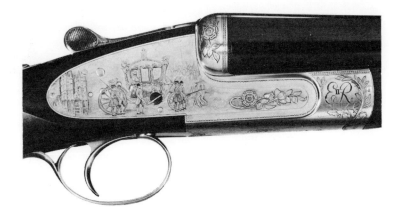

CHAPTER 1

'LONDON BEST'

It is no accident that the most exquisite shotguns in the world, more objects of fine art than mere weapons of the chase, have been brought to their present perfection by craftsmen in England. More surprisingly, the skill that makes them has, for two hundred years, largely centred in London. It reached its apogee with the coming of the breechloader in the nineteenth century.

From the fourteenth to the middle of the seventeenth century, the mystery of gunmaking was the reserve of master armourers on the mainland of Europe. It was they who evolved the fowling piece from the matchlock into the wheel lock, from the wheel lock through various modifications into the flint gun. In those times the English had none of the genius in mechanical expertise which distinguished the German and Italian artificers. From the seventeenth to the early eighteenth century, the Spanish forged, bored and twisted the most superior gun barrels in Europe. Throughout the seventeenth century Italian gunmakers (the Comminazzo family in Brescia were among the most celebrated) produced arms 'of a grace and lineal harmony' which, in the words of a modern collector, represent 'the best and most artistic decorative craftsmanship ever applied to firearms.'

Henry VIII was interested in casting cannon for his ships of war; but small arms, such as they were at the time, were imported. It is unlikely that King Henry even considered them as weapons of the chase which he associated with the pageantry of falconry and the bow. Elizabeth I is said to have had thirty-seven gunsmiths at work in the Minories in London, but a Dutchman was put in charge of them. An ardent hunter, Good Queen Bess put her trust in the long bow when deer were driven past her in the parks of her nobility.

There was a hint of things to come in Stuart times. In the first quarter of the seventeenth century Gervaise Markham published the first English manual which mentioned the sporting gun but it set forth in detail the best ways of taking every kind of feathered fowl by the use of snares and nets, of decoys of bird lime, and only incidentally introduced the birding-piece to the traditional methods for filling the pot. He belonged to the school, fashionable at the time, which recommended that the best fowling piece 'hath the longest barrel, being five foot and a half, or six feet long'. He established a fallacious notion, which has persisted almost up to the present time, that the longer the barrel, the nearer the hunter gets to his quarry, so the better his gun will be.

During the Civil War in England, hand guns were generally available and plain arms were blacksmithed. Although there are indications that superior ones might have been fashioned during the seventeenth century it is probable that the better ones, in the hands of Cavaliers like Prince Rupert, were brought from the continent. It is interesting that, in the King's cause, some of the best marksmen, keepers on the estates of the beleaguered nobility, used sporting smooth-bored guns, loaded as we may suppose, with swan shot and heaven knows what else besides.

As in all wars it was a bad time for game conservation. Trees were felled for their timber. Game was slaughtered by soldiers and poachers and private estates were ravished. Nevertheless, new developments in sporting arms were hastened. The pressure of war has always heralded new advances in weaponry and, although it is no part of this book, in medicine as well.

Until around 1637, England had no Gunmakers' Company established like the venerable Guilds of the Fletchers and the Bowyers. She had greater faith in her archers, although there is reason to suppose that primitive cannon were used at the Battle of Crecy in 1346.

Even after the formation of the Gunmakers' Company, charged with proving and testing firearms, most weapons were imported. Many weapons of the period, stamped though they are with the London mark, were only finished in London workshops. The English mark had no credit except that it conferred a comparative degree of personal safety.

The first of the great pride of English gunmakers emerged in the latter part of the eighteenth century. Significantly, it happened at a time when the murmurs of the French Revolution gave warning of the turmoil which was to envelop Europe intermittently for the next twenty-five years. It was a period in which Britain increasingly had to look to her own resources, and her own inventive genius. It is a paradox that while the British infantryman was fighting Napoleon with the clumsy 'Brown Bess' musket the English gunmakers, largely in London workshops, were bringing rifles, duelling pistols and sporting arms to a new peak of functional and aesthetic efficiency. Cut off from the continent the London craftsmen began to create weapons which, in the field of sport, have never been surpassed and are not yet superseded.

Years after Waterloo, the Duke of Wellington was attributed with the remark that we would have won the battle twice as quickly if we had had a company of long bowmen. A fair comment, after the event. There was no constraint against experiment among the London gunmakers. Their 'patents', many of them no more than self-advertisement, proliferated. In exuberant competition, within fifty years of Waterloo, they perfected the 'London Best' sporting gun as it is still made today without essential variations or even better performance.

The gunmakers were supported by the nineteenth-century sportsmen who were eager to make use of every 'improvement' that was offered. The military staggered on to the holocaust of the Crimea, reluctant as ever to accept new ways. Sportsmen acted differently.

The climate, during the Regency and after, could not have been more favourable for the enterprise of the sporting gunmakers. The continent was in disarray. Britain, unravished by war, was moving forward into a long era of peace, world power and prosperity. In a mood of prodigious national confidence, not unexpected after the interminable wars, gentlemen pursued a life of energetic leisure. Beau Brummell ruled the Assembly Rooms in the fashionable spa of Bath. The prince Regent, amid the oriental splendour of his Pavilion at Brighton, chanced a toe in the sea. And in the coaching age, and later the railway age, country house life flourished in England as never before.

London in 'The Season' assumed a status, which even now it has hardly lost, as the city of men. St James's became the enclave of strictly masculine clubs. It was around St James's that men gathered to find the best tailors, the best hatters and shirtmakers, the best fishing tackle, the best wines, the best bespoke riding boots, and the best sporting guns.

An old cobbler in the area once told me that, in 1914, they all knew in Jermyn Street that war was imminent because so many German cavalry officers came to London to order spare pairs of riding boots. Significantly, when the Soviet leaders came to England, the loot they looked for was a matched pair of Purdey guns.

In the heyday of the nineteenth century, 'London finish' became a term for fine leather goods. Sotheby's and Christie's emerged as the fashionable auction rooms for connoisseurs of the arts. A man of fashion scarcely had cause to cross Mayfair into the largely female world beyond. All around you could watch in shop windows industrious gunsmiths filing metal in their vices. London gunmakers, with magic names like Manton and Egg, Nock and Lancaster, Purdey and Boss, brought to London the craftsmanship developed over centuries in Europe. It is good to know that some of the names still survive.

The purchase of a London Best gun has never been a counter transaction. You can get good shotguns elsewhere as you might buy any other piece of furniture. In the shops of the great gunmakers of London it is still a ceremony, the purchase of an heirloom. To build it to your own measurements as conscientiously as a Saville Row suit will take months, these days even years. On past form, it will be worth twice what you paid for it before another generation takes over.

In the nineteenth century, 'anti-blood sport' societies were unheard of. The proper pursuits of a gentleman were hunting, fishing and shooting—the image of war, as Mr Jorrocks remarked—with only twenty-five per cent of its danger. They all drank too much port and madeira. They sat down to great meals of a dozen courses, and they kept their livers in order in the saddle. They angled in chimney-pot hats with vast fishing rods and horsehair lines, happily up to their thighs in ice cold trout and salmon waters. They shot, often from horseback in the partridge manors, walking up in the pheasant coverts and rabbit warrens, and enjoying acute discomfort in wintry weather on the mudflats and saltings of the coast. It was not only the men. Surtees's heroine, the beautifully named Lucy Glitters, is evidence that, far from fainting with the vapours, the belles of the foxhunting field were as hard as horse nails themselves.

The shotgun was made for the English rural scene, a rich green landscape of small hedged fields dotted with tidy woodlands, marl pits and spinneys, decorated with golden cornfields

Purdey's shop in 1826

James Purdey 1784–1863

By Royal Appointment since 1825

James Purdey (1784–1863) began his career as a stocker for the legendary Joseph Manton. In 1826 he took over Manton's old premises in Oxford Street. In 1881, with an expanding business, the spacious premises of Audley House were built which Purdey and Sons have occupied ever since. Generations of Purdeys presided over the firm until 1957. Remarkably the detailed records of gun sales have been preserved since the first gun was numbered early in the nineteenth century. The Royal Warrants, a volume of them, include all the crowned heads of Europe

Detailed records of gun sales

Purdey's shop in 1980

and coloured by a patchwork of kale, turnip and mustard. It was essentially a man-made countryside. The marshlands which the Romans found all over the country had been drained. The forests which the Normans conquered had been largely felled. Over the centuries England had been cultivated into a garden.

In new countries and wilder ones, other weapons have suited man's purpose. The opening of the early settlements in western North America was made possible by the rifle and, more important, Samuel Colt's development of the revolver. Incidentally, barbed wire, an American invention, played a significant part as well in controlling the buffalo at the same time that Colt's .45 beat the Red Indians' bows and arrows. That, and the sinking of wells driven by wooden mills in the prairies, led to the development of the West. In another continent, the opening of dark Africa was brought about by the hunting rifle.

In England, this green and pleasant land, the single-bulleted weapon was unwelcome after the Civil War. In a crowded landscape, miniature by comparison with the vast expanses of the Americas and Africa, it had no place.

It was also unnecessary. England was rich in fur and feather. It had no large mammals. Since the last wild boar was exterminated, somewhere between the fourteenth and sixteenth centuries, there were no wild animals to fear or to control. As a result of the extensive working of the land an enormous population of birds, hares and rabbits proliferated on the bounty of the agricultural crops. The shotgun, with an effective range of pellets between forty to sixty yards, was the ideal weapon to harvest them for the table.

In the early days of firearms, matchlocks were first used by the peasants, rather than the gentry, as a more effective alternative for killing wildfowl than nets and gins. It was only in the late seventeenth century, when falconry was on the wane, that the use of the gun became a gentleman's interest.

Increasingly, especially under the influence of eighteenth-century landscape gardeners like 'Capability' Brown, estates were planted which provided harbour for game. Small coverts made it easier to handle the crop. Lakes were flooded, not only for their aesthetic appearance, but also to attract wildfowl.

The shooting man who shot for recreation, as distinguished from the hunter in other parts of the world who shot for his dinner, came into being. It was not a wasteful operation. The game was harvested like the corn for the barn. It was treated as another food crop as indeed it was. In the passage of time game came to be reared like the seed of wheat, oats and barley. It provided a test of shooting skill for the landlord and his friends. It was also preserved, ruthlessly up to the end of the nineteenth century, against two-legged poachers to make sure that the culling did not reduce the stock on the ground.

In this work, I have traced this important aspect of English social history, and shown how the shotgun has influenced the customs and manners of our time. A socialist will say that it has been for the worse. In an industrial society, country life and the world of agriculture, has been dismissed as an anachronism by the people who live in urban areas. The shotgun, with the right to use it in the field, has been called the weapon of the privileged few. In a sense it is.

One reason why this country is so rich in wildlife is that so much of the land is still in private hands. In other countries, where anybody who buys a gun licence may shoot, game is scarce. In Latin countries especially, even song birds are at risk. In some countries, where the discipline of the field is not enforced, human fatalities are formidable. There is a hazard in the use of lethal weapons which is unavoidable. In England, we have evolved a system of conduct which has reduced the danger to a minimum. But the prejudice against the man with a gun under his arm, or a horse between his legs, persists. It is peculiar to England.

Only in England do you find that curious suspicion which makes the man on foot distrust the man on horseback. In Spain, for example, the caballero and, in South America, the gaucho are the very models of what proper men should be. In North America the cowboy legend of the man with a gun is part of the folklore of the country.

I trace the resentment in England to the Norman conquest. Only here do you find the illogical dislike of the horseman or the man, with the authority it confers, who carries a gun. It dates to a time when the privileged rode on horseback; when the Saxon, the man on foot, became the feudal serf of the conquerors who, on penalty of death, insisted on all the rights of venery for themselves. The ordinary man has never forgotten those hundreds of years when, as the underdog, he could not kill a deer without the risk of branding or worse, and raised sheep, pigs and oxen, only to stand by hungrily when they were served on the Norman's board, under their French names of mutton, pork and beef.

Deep in history, although few know why, the right to hunt, shoot and fish in England has been challenged ever since the days of Robin Hood. I make no apology for the fact that this book is for people who still have the good fortune to enjoy the land and its diversions.

The Bishop of Bond Street

Flamboyance is not the normal proof mark of the English gun trade. The gunmakers are largely distinguished by a reticence as secretive as that adopted by the waistcoated bespoke tailors, tape measures about their necks, who lurk behind cane-sheltered windows, in the same area of the West End of London, their only ostentation a Royal Coat of Arms.

An exception was William Bishop who in 1815 was appointed agent to Messrs Westley Richards, the Birmingham gunmakers, at 170 New Bond Street. For more than fifty years thereafter the Bishop of Bond Street was an institution of fashionable London, patronised by the nobility, cultivated by the Bond Street loungers who adopted a roll in their walk in 'the modern ease and fashion' and carried a toothpick between their teeth.

Bishop was an old hypocrite, with an ecclesiastical manner which earned him his title. His uniform was a broad-brimmed topper carefully ironed, a black swallow-tailed coat, a capacious white apron, and shirtsleeves turned over his forearm like the lawn of a high church dignitary. Although only half-literate, he had the gift of the gab and the voice to lay on the manner of a superior person of the cloth.

In the sacristy that was his shop he attracted the young bloods, officers and country squires. For their entertainment he would organise rat hunts, cock fights, a bout with the gloves or 'the raw 'uns' (bare fists), an hour's practice with the duelling pistol, or some other fashionable pastime. He became one of the well-known figures of the picaresque scene, so much so that it is reputed that when a growler was instructed by his fare to drive him to the Bishop of London, the cabby dropped him outside 170 Bond Street. 'What's this, cabby?' enquired the exasperated passenger. 'I told you the Bishop of London.' 'Well, can't you see him inside?' replied the cabby.

It is recorded in *The History of the Westley Richards Firm* that on another occasion, when he had arranged 'a mill' outside London for some of his cronies, the train in which he was

The Bishop of Bond Street
by William Salting, Manager of Weekes Robarts & Blondel, &c.
HENRY BARRAUD 1849

travelling was invaded by the police, rightly suspecting that a then illegal prize fight was planned. The bishop raised his hands in pious horror. 'Good gracious, what do you mean? We are going to the consecration of a new church.' Such was his aplomb and appearance that he got away with it.

Bishop was fond of dogs. He was so devoted to one named 'Tiny' that when she died, at the age of fifteen, he had a tomb made for her within the outer walls of 170 Bond Street sealed by a marble slab. At a time when dog-stealing was rife Tiny had been stolen, although later recovered. In his indignation the Bishop persuaded influential friends to introduce an Act of Parliament making the practice of dog-stealing an offence punishable by summary jurisdiction. It is said that his campaign to make his bill law cost him a thousand sovereigns.

To commemorate his efforts and the passage of the Dog Stealing Bill through Parliament, the Bishop's admirers and supporters presented him with his portrait (see page 16) displaying a gun in his shop with 'Tiny' and two other canine pets attending devotedly at his feet. A copy of the bust of his friend Colonel Peter Hawker is also in the picture.

More than anyone, the Bishop of Bond Street brought the tradition of fine workmanship in Birmingham to London. He was a born entrepreneur, even if an unlikely one.

(*Opposite*) The Bishop of Bond Street

'I like the power to shoot, even though I may not use it. The very perfection of our modern guns is to me one of their drawbacks; the use of them is so easy and so certain of effect that it takes away the romance of sport. There could be no greater pleasure to me than to wander with a matchlock through one of the great forests or wild tracks that still remain in England.'

RICHARD JEFFERIES

CHAPTER 2

LIFE IN AN AQUATINT

Sporting prints, alive today on the walls of every decent country pub and still ornamenting almost every country house, recall a remarkable century in English rural history. They belong to the short age of coaching before the railways took over. They span the gap from the daguerreotype to the invention of photography; from the flintgun, which had survived for two hundred years, to the early development of the breechloader. They are a record of change in which 'sporting' evolved as a fashionable recreation.

The hand-coloured pictures were the popular art of a period which extends from the late eighteenth to the last quarter of the nineteenth century. The method of reproduction was by woodcut, etching, line engraving and mezzotint, followed by stipple, aquatint and lithography. In this form of graphic expression the coloured aquatint is the authentic interpretation of the sporting scene of its times.

The prints are essentially primitives. They were largely created by enthusiastic, rather than great artists, who dedicated them exuberantly to their patrons among the nobility and members of their own sporting societies. The most familiar to us now are the productions of the Pollards (Robert, 1755–1839 and James, 1797–1876), the Alkens (Samuel, 1750–1815 and Henry, 1784–1851), and Sawray Gilpin (1733–1804). There were many others, some as distinguished as George Morland (1763–1894), working in the same medium.

The black and white prints were coloured by hacks, each allotted a brush in red, yellow, green or blue, which they laid on in the appropriate spaces designated by the artist. The quality of this mass-production work is inevitably inconsistent. The best of the sporting prints are enchanting. The worst are little more than forgeries. You can only use your own judgement to assess their individual quality. Their importance is that they tell us how our forbears in the early nineteenth century went about their sport.

The old gunners with their muzzleloaders had no conception of shooting what we now call 'driven game'. They usually hunted in pairs. With pointers ranging in front of them in the stubbles, with spaniels searching in covert, they shot at going-away birds with a single blast of black powder. The heavy cloud of smoke blinded their eyes for a second shot. Consequently, although double-barrelled shotguns were an early innovation of the nineteenth-century gunmakers, few used them. You will not meet double-barrelled guns in the hands of the sportsmen in the prints.

You will notice that they always held their guns with their hands short on the fore-end, the opposite of modern practice, because with good reason they feared a burst barrel. It was no way to balance a gun, but it served them for going-away shots when they only had to lay the barrel for a lift on to the target. They undoubtedly had skills, which we have lost, to correct their aim with a flintgun in which there is a tenth of a second time lag between trigger-pulling and ignition. No sporting print exists, to my knowledge, in which the shooter is attempting a bird flying towards him. No doubt, with a lucky shot, sportsmen achieved it. With a bit of luck, with an old flintgun, I have actually attained it myself. But, in the early nineteenth century, oncoming birds had no place in the order of the day.

Contemporarily, when the shotgun has been made as perfect for its limited purpose as it will ever need to be, it is well to look back on how it was, in a world little more than a hundred and fifty years ago, when the weapon first entered a new dimension.

Shooting in a chimney pot hat was a hazardous business. It is absurd but true that in all the coloured prints the sporters wear their tall hats. It was simply one of the mad hatter fashions of sporting in its time. I can recognise the importance of a pot hat to an angler as a substitute for a landing net. But in thick cover it must surely have been an embarrassing inconvenience to an eager shooter. Nevertheless, that is apparently what they wore. With heavy frocked coats bagged down with the rain and the dew, and buttoned gaiters like gutters about their legs, they were shooting in a climate in which, with wet flints and damp powder, it was always problematical; indeed it was questionable when they pulled the triggers, whether their guns would even fire.

The risks of a misadventure were considerable. When he sallied forth, the shooter had to load his waist with a flask of powder, a pouch of lead shot, and wadding for the charge. The prudent man with a muzzleloader (although many used dry grass for wadding and measured out their powder in the bowl of a clay pipe), had spring measures fitted into flask and pouch so that he could pour the correct load of powder and shot. But it was all wildly experimental; a matter of personal opinion on what suited the gun best. As powder was unpredictable in its performance, and shot was uncertain in size, every sportsman fancied himself as his own best judge.

The accessories for the proper use of a muzzle-loading flintgun filled the sportsman's pockets. The shooter needed oiled tow to ram home the powder charge firmly into the breech. If he was careful he punched a pasteboard card to hold the lead shot in position above the powder. It was important that he should carry essential accessories in order to deal with emergencies, just as we do when touring in our motor cars today. The first such tool

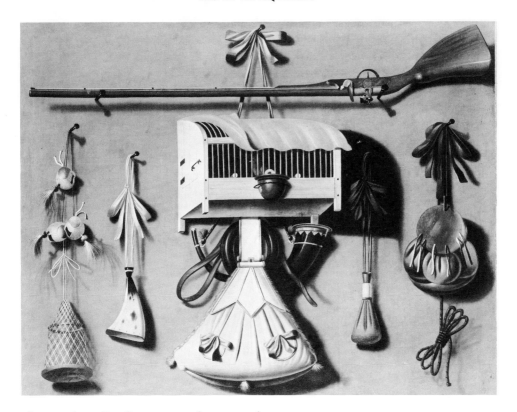

The paraphernalia of a seventeenth-century shot
This Dutch still-life illustrates the gear which the early gunners took into the field. The cage was
for a call bird used to attract the wild ones within range of the gun. The flasks were for powder
and shot. I cannot justify the necessity for a hunting horn, but the artist has always had his licence

was the turnscrew. This was necessary to release the screw in the teeth of the hammer of the
gun when the flint, or its position needed changing. Flints were as unpredictable in performance as sparking plugs used to be in cars.

A good flint, of the black transparent kind which was mined and knapped at Brandon on
the Suffolk-Norfolk border, might last forty shots. A bad one would crumble after ten.
There was an art in setting it, screwed in with a pad of leather or lead as a cushion, so that
when it hit the frizzen pan it gave a fat spark. New flints were put in flat side upwards.
Worn flints had to be jiggered about 'to save vexation and loss of time'.

Most shooters carried spare flints against misfires. If they were wise they also equipped
themselves with a sharp-pointed feather to clear touchholes gummed up with the residue of
exploded black powder. They pulled the triggers on their guns with a certain optimism.
They reloaded with a remarkable disregard of the perils.

The hazards of the sport with a muzzleloader were formidable. In the excitement of the
chase sportsmen fired their ramrods after departing game. In the hurry to reload after a
hangfire, which was common, there was always the danger of looking down the barrel to

Powder flasks

Shot pouches

Knapped flints

see what had gone wrong, and catching a charge in the face. If powder was poured into the barrel over a winking spark after shooting, flasks were liable to blow up.

Gameshooting at the beginning of the nineteenth century was largely experimental, both on the part of gunmakers and shooters. It was, at best, a messy business. The elegantly dressed characters in the sporting prints came home with blackened hands and faces, sooted and smelling like their guns with the oily residue of black powder. After twenty rounds or so their guns coked up like old tobacco pipes. Their hats, after a season in the field, smelt like exploded rockets.

Double-barrelled guns, an early innovation of the gunmakers, were doubly dangerous. It was so easy to double-charge one barrel Shooters were recommended to protect themselves by leaving the ramrod in the barrel they had charged before pouring powder into the other.

The early percussion guns in which the charge was exploded by a fulminate inside a copper cap, instead of a flint, were possibly more dangerous than the well-tried method of the past. The patent for the Rev Alexander Forsyth's detonating gun as it was called, was registered in 1807. But it was not until 1820–30, after a flush of other patents, that most of the conversions from flintlock to percussion were made. The early copper caps were so unreliable that the most handsome claim of the manufacturers was that they would not blow up in your face.

Early writers tried to regulate shooting practice to reduce the risks. After expounding their theories on the correct measurements of shot and powder for different bores, largely founded on personal theory, they recognised a starting list of 'don'ts'. It is interesting that they regarded it as dangerous to carry a muzzleloader, as we carry breechloaders today, in the crook of the arm. They reckoned that the safer way was over the shoulder. But they also recommended heating black powder before shooting in plates 'too hot to hold'. It is proper to add that they cautioned it should be done away from open fires and candles. They

A box for percussion caps

gave instructions for loading, fair enough when men had to push powder and shot down the business end of a barrel, which make me wince. It was never safe; but they were a courageous lot.

I often think of the shooters coming home after their days in field, covert and marsh, with their stinking guns and small prize of game, as if I had lived with them. No self-respecting housewife can have allowed the guns into the house. They had to be scrubbed out with cold water, and then hot water from a kettle. The percussion guns, due to the corrosion of the caps, had to be cleaned even more thoroughly than the flintguns. When the guns were cleaned the gunner himself equally needed a scour in the hip-bath.

It is possible to live again the world of the sporting prints using a muzzleloader today. The safe way is to use replicas, which are increasingly manufactured. The Japanese are currently making a game of shooting with reproductions of matchlocks; the Americans practise with modern versions of the Kentucky rifle and various Colts. I have seen a matched pair of flintlock guns, built by a modern maker for an eccentric sportsman, which looked good enough. They patterned abominably because contemporary barrelmakers have lost the secrets which the old craftsmen had of relieving the barrels at breech and muzzle. Remarkably, as I shall explain later, there are still no rules of engineering in the boring of a shotgun barrel. Its performance rests entirely on the uncanny accuracy of a craftsman's eye.

My own taste is that there is no pleasure in handling imitations of the past. For me the charm is to handle the stuff of history—to warm my palms on the burnished walnut of an old stock, to listen to the sweet double click of the action of a period lock, to put straight powder through the beautiful figuring of Damascus barrels. But it calls for care.

I quote a passage from one of my own books, *English Sporting Guns and Accessories*, 1969, now out of print, because I wrote it when I was regularly using a muzzleloader in the field:

> In all shooting there is an unavoidable element of risk. With old muzzleloaders, in which the metal of the barrel is almost certainly 'tired', the danger is greater. It could not be otherwise in a thing which has so far outlasted the human brain and muscle which created it. Handling muzzleloaders calls for very conscious discipline and attention to firing detail.

There is little doubt that the old sportsmen took risks. In many cases they suffered the consequences from burst barrels, powder flasks blowing up in their hands, and charges going off in their faces. It is also true that others who spilt powder and shot into their guns, as liberally as some scoop mustard on to their dinner plates, got away with it. Black powder, as devilishly combustible outside a gun barrel as modern smokeless powders are relatively innocent until they are put inside one, can be exploded, as any firework addict knows, from a paper tube. The hazard in an old gun comes when a charge of lead is put on top of the powder. With the increase it creates in pressure it is well to remember the admonition on the Roman Candle. After lighting the blue touch-paper, retire immediately.

In self-preservation, if you are firing a gun which has probably been silent for a hundred

(Opposite top) Out of the Mist—Grouse, a watercolour by Rodger McPhail
(Below) Pinkfeet—Wild Geese, a watercolour by Rodger McPhail

years, lash it to a fence or, better, a heavy tripod of the type used for sawing logs. You can test it with a light charge by pulling the trigger at the end of a long piece of string. Theoretically, the weapon should first be taken to a gunsmith to remove the breech-plugs and make an assessment of its condition. In practice he will not be able to give more than qualified approval. But you can proof it youself by remote control, aiming the barrels at sheets of newspaper—which will show how the shot is patterning—and increasing the powder charge until you can reasonably take the risk of bringing the gun to your shoulder. When the gun is in your hands, however confident you feel, resist the temptation of loading a full charge. It is dangerous, and not even necessary. A muzzleloader of 14-bore, the equivalent of the modern 12-bore breechloader, will throw a killing pattern with two drams (or drachms as it used to be spelt) of powder and an ounce of shot.

The correct balance of the charge will vary from gun to gun because muzzleloaders, whatever their nominal bores, are individuals. When you use one you must discover the mean charge of powder and shot which suits it; and suits you. Reading what the old gunners pontificated can be utterly confusing because shot sizes in their day were not uniform, and powder was variable in its efficiency. The contemporary shot with a light muzzleloader will do well to stick to No 5 or No 6 shot, and trust to light charges of powder, powder which is far more regular than anything they knew at the beginning of the nineteenth century.

Rising With Vigour—Woodcock, a watercolour by J. C. Harrison

(Left) *Turning Away*—Woodcock,
a watercolour by J. C. Harrison

(Below) *Mallard Getting Up*—
a watercolour by J. C. Harrison

A Partridge Year—Charles Tunnicliffe

(*Opposite top*)
A Bouquet of Pheasants—a watercolour by J. C. Harrison
(*Below*)
Covey Rising—French Partridge, a watercolour by Rodger McPhail

Imperial Metal Industries (Kynoch) Ltd sell four types of black powder today, graded by quality and grain size. TS2 and TS6 are best quality, types F and FFF are lower quality. TS2 or FFF should be used for 12-bore and smaller gauges, TS6 or F for 10-bore and larger.

A gun can be 'chambered' for the shot charge that suits it by slipping an overcard into the mouth of the barrel. The load of pellets that settles evenly over the card is likely to be the best one for the gun. For overpowder wads in a 14-bore, I cut 12-bore felts, chewing them in my teeth so that they ram smoothly into the barrel. The old gunners favoured a bit of dry grass or tow to tamp the shot down. I prefer a bit of crumpled newspaper for the pyro-technic effect it produces when the gun is fired.

Flintguns in shootable condition are necessarily rarer than percussion arms; but they still exist. The trouble is to obtain reliable flints. Gun flints are still knapped at Brandon in Suffolk, but most of them are now so soft that the gunner is unlikely to get more than four or five shots from them. But I have flints now, transparent black flints specially knapped for one of my own guns, which are good for twenty shots. The art of getting good performance is to mount the flint, with a piece of leather behind it, flat side upwards in the jaws of the cock so that it strikes evenly on the frizzen. After wear, it can be turned over. Suffice that there is a craft in settling a flint efficiently which provides a satisfaction of its own.

By comparison, mounting copper caps on the nipples of a percussion gun has no problems. The snag, with both forms of ignition, is that they don't work unless touchholes and nipples are kept scrupulously free from blockage. No accessory is more useful to the modern muzzleloading enthusiast than a woman's hairpin to push powder and fulminate waste out of the way. And there is no duty more rewarding in result than thorough gun-cleaning.

A flintgun can be orphaned from care, reddened with the rust from powder residue, without coming to much harm. A percussion gun, poisoned with the chemicals from the cap, can go to pot very quickly without constant attention. But neither sort of gun will give a good performance in the field without thorough nannying. Oiling and polishing, useful enough, are far less important than the scouring and pumping out of the barrels with libations of cold water, followed by hot to steam them dry.

(*Opposite*) **Every shooting man should recognise these proof marks on English guns**
The Birmingham Proof House
1 Marks which show that the gun is proved *for black powder only*, and is therefore unsafe under the additional pressure of modern nitro powders. Guns carrying these marks date to 1904, when the crowned mark changed, to the BV BP NP type below
2 The series of marks introduced in February, 1955, which gives details of service pressure to the square inch. The mark at the bottom left corner—in this case LBI—is the private viewer's mark which in code gives the name of the viewer who passed the gun and the year in which it was proved
The London Proof House
3 These marks show that the gun has been proved *for black powder only*. They are found on guns made as late as 1925; but if you see them it generally means proof before 1896. It is dangerous to shoot cartridges loaded with nitro powder through these barrels.
4 Guns carrying these London marks were proved between 1925 and 1955. From left to right, the marks read: Provisional proof, bore size, view mark, definitive proof, nominal bore size, chamber length, nitro proof mark, maximum charge of shot in ounces

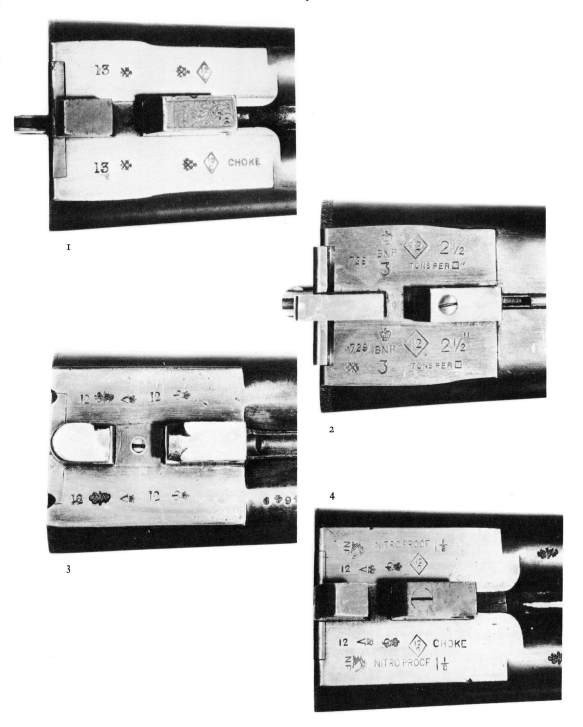

1

2

3

4

Proving gun barrels at Birmingham

Modern cleaning equipment, although it should be kept apart from the jags and brushes used for breechloaders, is ideal for the job. The important thing, as you pump the rod, is to force the black and oily residue through the touch-holes and the nipples until the water spouts clean.

The loading principle for both flint and percussion is the same. The heel of the weapon should be firmly seated against the left boot. The barrels in the left hand should be pushed at the full length of the left arm into the stand-at-ease position. The object of the exercise is to keep your head out of the way if the gun goes off unexpectedly.

If it is a double-barrelled gun, drop the ramrod into the empty barrel before you pour powder into the other. This is to prevent the notorious error of double-charging. Ram the powder down hard with the wad, and, when you have measured the shot, wad it down lightly—just enough to keep it in position in the barrel.

Remember all the risks; double loading doubles the danger. A spark in the chamber from a previous shot can explode the powder as you pour it in. Make sure that your gun is never at full cock, especially when loading, and generally until you mean to fire. If you suspect you have made a mistake, draw the charge with the wormscrew which is normally fitted under the brass nose of the ramrod.

The stateliest shop

It is said that, when James Purdey established his business in South Audley Street his notion was that, if it failed, it could be re-established as a picture gallery. It is now both a picture gallery and museum of the great shots of two centuries. It has become a sanctum of a sporting tradition. All who enter tread reverently here

33

This collection of over a thousand cartridges, each one with the name of a different maker, has been assembled by Mr Carey Keates of Messrs Holland & Holland. It is certain that, in the future, the coloured paper cases of a past age will become, as memorabilia, as valuable as cigarette cards or stamps

It is useful to add that, among the risks for the guns themselves, you will almost certainly shatter the hammers of a detonator if you release the action on the nipples of an empty arm. You can spark an empty flintlock because the frizzen affords the necessary resistance. When any old gun comes into your hands, begin by searching it with the ramrod to make sure that some slaphappy sportsman in the past hasn't left a charge in it. It can happen; it has happened to me.

It may be that the reader will conclude that I have over-estimated the hazards of shooting with these old guns. It is the safeway to introduce them. But I wouldn't be writing this at all if I weren't the victim of their seductive charms. I am one who makes no apology for a love affair with history.

Those who are enmeshed in it move into a period where language was made which lives beyond the language of its sport. Who hasn't 'ducked the flash' as the wildfowl used to when the old muzzleloaders fizzed laboriously into action? Who hasn't enjoyed a 'dram', slang which dates from a time when a dram was not a measure of whisky but a measure of powder? Whose projects haven't 'hung fire' the way the muzzleloaders did?

'*When flint-guns were the order of the day few sporting gentlemen of distinction ever thought of anything but the gun of a first-rate maker, for the simple reason that*—on the goodness of the work *depended the* quickness in firing, *and consequently the* filling of the bag. *But,* now-a-days, *every common fellow in a market-town can detonate an old musket, and make it shoot as quick as can be wished; insomuch that all scientific calculations in shooting,* at moderate distances, *are now so simplified that we, every day, meet with jackanapes—apprentice boys who can shoot flying, and knock down their eight birds out of ten.*'

LT-COL PETER HAWKER

(*Opposite*) Bust of Lt-Col Peter Hawker

CHAPTER 3

THE FATHER
OF GAMESHOOTING

Marching through the first half of the nineteenth century a remarkable sportsman became at once the voice and the guide of the master craftsmen of London. Lt-Col Peter Hawker has fair claim to be named the father of game gun shooting. In a period of climacteric change in weaponry he pioneered a code of practice in the field, and conferred on the shotgun the accolade of social acceptability.

He published the first edition of his famous book *Instructions to Young Sportsmen in all that relates to Guns and Shooting* in 1814 after being wounded at the Battle of Talavera in the Peninsular War. The tenth revised version was published posthumously, with an introduction by his son, in 1854. The period, in which the book was never out of print, covers the transition from the flintgun to the detonators and the early breechloaders.

Hawker's work, read as it should be in conjunction with his personal diaries kept over a period of fifty years (first published in two volumes in 1892), is a notable sporting record. Hawker introduced methods of wildfowling which are still accepted. He also laid down principles for shooting game on the wing. His own inventive contribution to gun design, and his patronage of the gunmakers of his day, confirmed the reputation of English and, in particular, London workmanship.

Because he lived in a time of radical change in firearm design, his opinions, and he was very opinionated, depend on which of the ten editions of his book falls into the reader's hands. For years he believed that flintguns, which he had grown up with, were superior to detonators. No doubt his old flintguns were indeed superior to the first percussion arms, just as for a time muzzleloaders were more reliable than early breechloaders.

Inevitably Hawker had imitators. He was apoplectic about his contemporaries like Captain Lacy (1842) who he regarded as a copyist of his own work. In a sense that was true although Lacy wrote rather more stylistically than Hawker. Nevertheless, whatever Hawker lacks in literary polish, his was unquestionably the first text book. And no writer, however literate, can deny him the olive branch. The epitaph he composed for the tombstone of his friend Joseph Manton, the great nineteenth-century gunmaker, might with minor alterations have well been his own. You will still read it on a tablet in the cemetery at Kensal Green:

In memory of Mr Joseph Manton, who died, universally regretted, on the 29th of June, 1835, age 69. This humble tablet is placed here by his afflicted family, merely to mark where are

(*Above*) Longparish House, Andover, Hampshire, drawn by Master Peter Hawker in the year 1798 when he was twelve years old

(*Opposite*) Hawker's family home, now the property of Colonel C. P. Dawnay, CBE, MVO as it looks today. The river Test is in the foreground

deposited his mortal remains. But an everlasting monument to his unrivalled genius is already established in every quarter of the globe, by his celebrity as the greatest artist in firearms that the world produced, as the founder and father of the modern gun trade, and as a most scientific inventor in these departments, not only for the benefit of his friends and the sporting world, but for the good of his King and country.

Joseph Manton built the guns; the gallant Peter Hawker taught his countrymen how to use them. The man who reveals himself in his book and in his diaries is a prototype; as real as Pepys, as ageless as Jorrocks, and as fallible as Mr Winkle.

Peter Hawker had that very characteristic English quality that he never grew up. All his life, he had the heart and enthusiasm and the intolerance of a boy. He boasted, as boys do, of his prowess. As boys do, he consistently over-tried his own strength. He quarrelled with sudden fury and rich expletives and made it up with his enemies as easily as a boy tempted by the sight of a humbug.

His feud with 'the green-livered son of a b – – – –, the lawyer' was typical. The lawyer, who is not named in the diary, was the chief object of Peter Hawker's hate for seven or eight shooting seasons; his only crime, so it appears, was being a neighbour as keen on partridge shooting as Hawker himself. Every September, from 1832 onwards, Hawker has something to say about him:

September 2, 1832: The masterly manner in which I outmanoeuvred the green-livered lawyer and his gang was even better sport than the shooting itself.

September, 1834: We had our usual spree outflanking and racing round the green-livered lawyer who had a whole platoon of cock-a-doodle shooters and did all he could to spoil our sport.

And so it goes on, season after season, until August 15, 1838, when Hawker records casually in his diary:

A reconciliation took place between me and my old enemy, the lawyer, so that all scrambles and skirmishes in the field of sport will be happily at an end; and they would never have occurred at all but for the mischief-making lies of gamekeepers, who have since left the lawyer's service.

It is notable that the literary style of Hawker's diaries, from 1802–53, shows no marked change. His interests, and his attitude, when he was sixteen, and in what he called his 'second season of sporting' and when he was dying in his sixty-seventh year, are identical. '*A beautiful day,*' he writes in his diary during his last illness:

'Crossed to Yarmouth, and got driven to Freshwater for the fine sea air, but too weak to walk along the cliffs. Lots of gents popping at rock-birds and rifling the cormorants, and rookeries being stormed inland. All to tantalise me, like the gents having good sport angling the other day in view of my windows at Longparish, and I too ill to go out.

Hawker wrote of his own great life interests that he was 'shooting mad and mad on music'. He was, in fact, an accomplished amateur musician, an ardent concertgoer and a fan of the great ('I heard with ecstasy the wonderful Paganini') and, characteristically, he wrote, besides his celebrated *Instructions to Young Sportsmen*, another work called *Instructions for the Best Position on the Pianoforte*.

Hawker's zest for living, coupled with his superb belief in himself, obviously inspired everybody he met. Shooting and music were his chief passions ('badgered away from a batch of Beethoven to go after a cursed cock pheasant that I never found'), but Peter Hawker was interested in everything. Throughout the whole of his diaries, you find him hopping about like a small boy who cannot find the time to spare to go to the lavatory.

On like a mad dog from morning till night with Captain Shrapnel, my old friend the General's son, with gun-makers, projectilists, general officers, ordnance authorities, engineers, etc., on the subject of arms and national defence.

Up by candlelight again, and out till three, when the tide would no longer serve: but never had a chance as the geese were too much persecuted to venture near the shore, and the sea was too rough to come near them afloat.

Persecuted with printers, and other bothering book-fellows, in the city all day; and then on from half-past three in the afternoon till three o'clock after midnight compiling fair a list of contents, plates, and various other matters for my book. Who would be an author?

Author, musician, inventor, and the leading shooting man of his day, Peter Hawker was also a keen farmer, an enthusiastic angler, major and later lieutenant-colonel of the North Hampshire Militia, and, finally, deputy lieutenant of his county. He could sketch sufficiently well to keep a record of what he had seen. He loved foreign travel and, or course, detested foreign countries:

After the account we had heard of Valognes, and knowing it be be one of the first towns in Normandy, we at least expected to see something decent; but of all the filthy, ugly, dirty, miserable places I ever saw, I may name this as one of the most abominable.

He was desperately patriotic and made a point of getting a good seat for all royal processions, coronations, marriages and funerals. He had this to say of William IV's Coronation in 1831 which he watched, with his family, from the windows of the United Services Club:

I never saw so many people together in my life, nor did I ever before witness so grand a cortege. The state carriage surpassed description for its happy combination of profuse splendour and chaste good taste. I never before saw a procession of such excessive finery without some approach to what is tawdry. But here everything was good taste in the extreme.

Unhappily, in 1851, he does not give us his opinion of the Crystal Palace, at which he himself was one of the exhibitors in the Great Exhibition. He was much too angry at missing a meeting with the Queen through 'the rascally injustice' of the officials. Indeed, he wrote a personal letter to Prince Albert protesting against 'the shameful neglect of the authorities'. It must have been a strong letter because, on October 14—one day before the Exhibition closed—he records, with deep emotion:

> I was honoured with a special interview on the subject of my new gun, not only with Prince Albert, but with Her Majesty also, and their affability was not a little flattering to a veteran amateur in gun-making.

It was probably his energetic interest in the technical improvement of firearms which kept his mind so surprisingly receptive, for an elderly country gentleman, to all the new inventions of the Victorian age. He was an enthusiastic railway traveller in his last years; his favourite phrase to describe his energetic daily round is 'railway speed'. He made a point of visiting all the manufactories for electro-plate, papier mâché, machinery and the rest; and, on one occasion, made a special visit to see the new gasometer supplying Birmingham.

His vitality, from the beginning of his life to the end, is breathtaking. Yet he suffered considerably from ill-health. He was occasionally incapacitated by his old wound which he received serving with distinction under Wellington. A bullet went clean through his thigh. But, most of the time, he suffered from another trouble which the doctors of the time appear to have been unable to diagnose. He constantly refers to it: 'sick as a dog', 'too weak to go out', 'unable to put pen to paper till this day from severe illness.' It made him, bless him, a bit of a hypochondriac. He is always 'quacking himself up' with some patent cure; but the only one that seems to work is when he takes his gun, or his punt, and pulls himself together with murderously hard exercise.

> *April 19, 1831:* A sharp frost and a north-easterly gale, which I had to face on the box all the way to London this day; and I am sure I owe my escape from ague to a hot bath, rhubarb and soda, by which I cheated the doctor out of at least £10, by finding myself all right the next morning.

His home throughout his life was at Longparish House, four miles east of Andover, Hampshire, on the banks of the Test; and, incidentally, it's enough to break a dry-fly angler's heart to read of the bags of great trout he hauled out of the river in every season of the year with worm, minnow, spinner and, failing all else, a drag-net. He also had a cottage at Keyhaven, near Lymington, which he visited every winter for the wildfowling, and a house in London, where he died.

Throughout the whole of his published diaries, there is, I think, only a single personal reference to his wife. Talking of a day's shooting in France he ends with the note:

> Finished my day with shooting the dog, at the express desire of Mrs Hawker, and to the great satisfaction of all who were with us.

The record of his shooting bag, summarised from the diaries, shows that between 1802–53, Hawker shot 17,753 head of different varieties of game. Of these, 7,035 were partridges,

Extract from Colonel Peter Hawker's Diary (September 17, 1827)

'Assembled my myrmidons for one more grand field day, in order to have some of their likenesses. Mr Childe (the artist) attended as a strict observer, and Mr Joseph Manton shot with me. Our united bag was 48 partridges and one hare, and we returned sometime before the day was over, on order that Mr Childe might complete by good daylight the necessary sketched of the group. My share of the bag was 28 partridges but had I shot entirely by myself, and been able to waive the usual ceremony of shooting in company, and galloped up all my birds, as heretofore, I am confident I should have killed 30 brace of birds'

In the engraving shown here, Hawker is on horseback and Joseph Manton the great gunmaker stands beside him

almost all of them killed in Hampshire; 575 pheasants, and 631 hares. His bag of swans, ducks and geese totals 4,488; including 2,211 wigeon, 1,327 brent and 38 whoopers. But the most remarkable feature of the bag is the scarcity under certain headings. Living in Hampshire, in a country of rich farmland and water meadows, Hawker records the killing of only 20 wood pigeons and 318 rabbits in his whole shooting career. He only got 16 grouse but then he went to Scotland only once and the grouse moors then were not what they are today.

It was Hawker's boast that he never came back from shooting with an empty bag. On one occasion at least, with the aid of an army of beaters, he shot fifty brace of partridges to his own gun in a day. He often went through the day without a miss. He invented the word 'cannon' to describe the feat when he deliberately brought down two out of a covey with a single shot; which, according to himself, he often did. Sir Ralph Payne-Gallwey, himself one of 'the ten best shots in England' in his own day, has gone on record with the statement that Peter Hawker, in the style of game shooting he pursued, has probably never been surpassed and that, as a single shot 'he has never been, and perhaps never will be, equalled.'

How Hawker achieved what he did, with a muzzleloader and, mostly, flint percussion guns, has never been satisfactorily explained. Hawker himself, referring to the time lag between the pulling of the trigger of a flint gun and the explosion of the charge, talks of birds 'ducking the flash'. Yet he shot on the wing and consistently put up such performances as killing fifteen snipe without a miss.

It has been argued, by way of explanation, that in Hawker's day, cover was thicker, the stubble stood higher, and birds were less wary. But there is not the slightest evidence to support it. On the contrary. In the latter years of his life, Hawker never ceases complaining of the scarcity and wildness of birds. He goes out all day to find a single cock pheasant reported on his land. He has to 'slave' for birds, and talks nostalgically of the old days when his men gave 'a butcher's halloa' for every twenty brace brought to bag. In addition, he makes it abundantly clear that the other shooters simply cannot compete with his own performance.

Although Hawker's skill with a flint-gun must always provide a fascinating subject for conjecture among shooting people, it is a pity that specialist interest in his achievements has tended to obscure the greater general significance of his diaries. Hawker was so much more than a crack shot. He was a colourful, lovable personality; the very model of a model country gentleman. And his diaries are a revelation of the country scene in his times.

'The art of shooting flying is arrived at tolerable perfection.'

THE SPORTSMEN'S DIRECTORY (1792)

(*Opposite*) Soldier firing semi-portable gun (from an early MS)

CHAPTER 4

AN EXPLOSION OF INVENTION

If Colonel Peter Hawker (1786–1853) had lived just ten years longer he would have witnessed a more revolutionary change in shooting practice than he ever foresaw in his life. Within a decade the shotgun was transformed from a weapon used solely to provide food for the table, into an instrument of skilled recreation. Driven gameshooting in Europe, with increasingly larger bags, became practical and fashionable. To understand how the change came about in such a short time it is relevant, first, to reconsider the shotgun's slow emergence into efficiency.

From the discovery of gunpowder in the smoky past the development of firearms stagnated for centuries. It is merely guesswork that the Chinese were the first to discover the explosive properties of saltpetre. It is certain that the only value of medieval cannon was that they had an element of surprise. Early hand guns, laboriously loaded and pointed over forked rests, were inferior to the crossbow, the pike or the long bow. It is surprising how late the sword and the axe commanded the battlefield as weapons of war.

The 'hand gonne' of the fifteenth century was little more than a squib. It lacked any sort of lock. The shooter was obliged to ignite it with one hand free to hold a smouldering match of tow steeped in saltpetre which, at the critical moment, he pushed into a touchhole drilled into the barrel. In the matchlock, a serpentine, which struck like a serpent, carried the match to the powder in the flash-pan.

In the sixteenth century the matchlock system was replaced by a crude form of flint-and-steel lock known as the snaphance, in which the use of the slow match as a means of ignition was superseded by the mechanical action of striking a flint sharply against a flat bed of steel, so held that the resulting sparks would fall into the flash pan and explode the gun. A

45

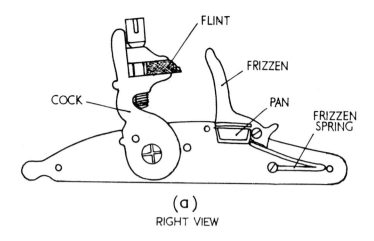

(a)
RIGHT VIEW

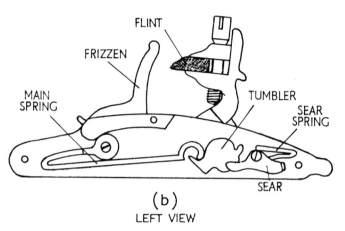

(b)
LEFT VIEW

The English flint-lock mechanism

modification called the wheel lock, which may be placed between 1510–20, was introduced by the gunsmiths of Nuremburg.

It was in the seventeenth century that 'the English flint-lock', which almost certainly originated on the continent, appeared. In use, a flint held in the jaws of a springed hammer, scraped against a curved steel pan-cover (the frizzen) which was thus thrown open, the spark igniting the priming powder which fired the charge. With modifications the flintgun survived until the middle of the nineteenth century.

From early times, the gunmakers of Europe were attracted by the possibility of making breechloading arms. They were called 'chamber pieces'. They failed because a fierce exchange of gas occurred at the junction of the chamber and the breech when the gun was fired. They had not learnt how to lock the action face and the breech safely together. Instead they concentrated craftsmanship in their guns on fine furnishing of gold and silver embellishments. They produced weapons, many with beautifully filed actions which contributed nothing to their functional performance. Their weapons were barrel heavy, the stocks were club ended, and balance, so important in a shotgun, was never considered at all.

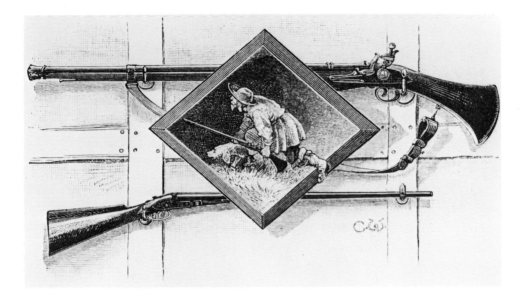

It was the English craftsmen, in the late eighteenth and early nineteenth centuries, who designed a shotgun which fell into the shoulder, and was contrived as an extenstion of the shooter's arms, a weapon with no unnecessary 'gingerbread'.

It will always be arguable which of the London craftsmen designed the character and shape of a beautiful weapon which is essentially unchanged today. Peter Hawker would have it that Joseph Manton was the founder and father of modern gunmaking. The probability is that he was one, just one, of the great innovators of the late eighteenth and nineteenth centuries. His guns anticipated the shape of guns up to the present time. No makers have improved on the shape of his gunstocks, or the relation of barrel to action.

Joseph Manton was an inventive genius but, in my opinion, he must take second place to his fellow tradesman, Henry Nock (1772–1804). Nock took out a patent incorporating a new sort of breech, a matter duly recorded on a gold shield, more correctly a poinçon, on the barrels of his guns. Anybody who studies nineteenth-century sporting arms soon recognises that patents of one sort or another were two-a-penny. Most of the patents claimed by rivalling gunmakers in a period of swift change were transitory and insignificant.

Henry Nock of London, with his patent of April, 1787, achieved a breakthrough. Prior to his patent, the plug at the base of the barrel of a muzzleloading gun was a solid lump of metal. What this meant was that, when the flint sparked the powder in the pan, the flame spurting into the touchhole ignited only a corner of the charge in the barrel. As a consequence it took longer for the powder to burn. In Nock's gun, the touchhole was pierced into the chamber in the centre of the charge with the result that the priming powder fired the middle of the charge. Guns shot harder and quicker. In fact, chambered guns were produced prior to Nock's patent; but his was the successful one.

After nearly two hundred years of comparatively static gun design, from the time when the flintlock superseded the matchlock, the wheel-lock and the snaphance, it was from

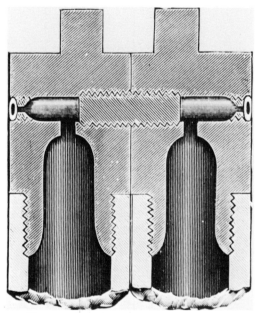

Nock's patent breech

Nock's patent that gun invention leapt forward. The immediate result of it, ensuring quicker burning of powder, was that it became possible to make an effective reduction of gun barrels from about 40in to 30in; to encourage a better-balanced half stocked weapon with the weight of metal in the middle, and to open the way for double-barrelled guns. At last shooting was not a matter of creeping in for a raking shot at low range, but a sport. From Nock's invention the way was open, from the clumsy long-barrelled weapons of Queen Anne's reign, to the evolution of the breechloaders.

There is no question that Joseph Manton was the master gunmaker of his time. The patronage of Colonel Peter Hawker has possibly enhanced his posthumous reputation. It is doubtful that he made better guns than his brother John, or the other great gunmakers of his period like Egg and Purdey. What he conferred on the gun trade was a matter of style. Joseph Manton's guns are the model of taste which has scarcely changed until now. He was the 'Savile Row' gunmaker. His mahogany stocks, beautifully squared, set into the shoulder. His 'elevating-rib' introduced a new dimension into shooting practice. He had other notions which were not quite so successful. But, in all his work, he was pointing the way to the modern shotgun.

Within a few years after Joseph Manton's death (1835) change was so rapid that it is no wonder that the nineteenth-century gunmakers produced a new patent every few years, or months. Bemused sportsmen had their guns changed again and again to bring them up to date with the latest invention. The result is that anyone today who is interested in the past, finds it difficult to distinguish between shotguns which have subsequently been faked or renovated, and guns which were converted, perhaps by the original maker, from flint to percussion, and even to dual purpose guns able to work with both systems.

The introduction of a new device did not mean that it was popularly accepted. On the contrary, it is safe to say that it was opposed. Colonel Peter Hawker had doubts that percussion was better than flint up to his death in 1853. Lord Walsingham, named in mid-Victorian times as one of 'the ten best shots in England', dismissed the introduction of Whitworth steel barrels, which duly replaced the twist of Damascus barrels, because he did not like the noise the charge made going up the spout.

It is true that we have lost, as we have gained, out of the past. Old muzzleloaders—although they take longer to charge, and require more knowledge in handling than breech-loading arms—shoot as far and as straight as contemporary weapons. The evolution of the sporting gun in England during the nineteenth century is one of the wonders of that remarkable age.

It is proper, in order to get a grasp of a complex phase of firearms development, to have a tabulation of dates. It is also important to recognise that innovations, however outstanding, were not generally accepted until decades after they were introduced. It is significant that, at the present time, there are still people—they are often gamekeepers—using guns, which they believe are the hardest hitting guns imaginable, but which have been proofed only for black powder. Under the extra pressures of smokeless powders, they ought to blow up in their owner's hands. It is to the lasting credit of the old craftsmen that somehow the guns stick together. Under the extra pressures of proof firing the barrels would certainly burst.

A hundred years saw the shotgun, (and incidentally other forms of artillery) pass from primitive beginnings to the precision instrument we know now. The breechloader replaced the muzzleloader. Steel barrels replaced the old twist. Centre fire cartridges succeeded the powder flask and the shot pouch. Smokeless powder made a formidable change in sporting practice because the shooter could at last see without a dark cloud blinding his second shot. Hammerless guns, or rather guns in which the hammers were enclosed inside the action, became the order of the day. Ejectors, which threw out the exploded cartridge cases, increased shooting speed to the point where an expert with two guns and a loader could shoot as fast as if he had a modern automatic in his hands. A period came in which England, and then Scotland, became the shotgun countries of the world.

Two significant developments, apart from Nock's patent breeching, sparked the way in the latter half of the eighteenth century to the explosive invention that followed. In 1782, William Watts, a Bristol plumber, discovered how to make drop shot (Patent No. 1347). It is said that the notion of spilling molten lead into water through a sieve from a height so that it formed like a raindrop came to him in a dream. Formerly shot had been cut out of strips into dice and rattled into rough spheres.

In 1815, Sir William Congreve, Comptroller of the Royal Laboratory at Woolwich, took out a patent (No 3937) to standardize powder. For the first time, gunpowder achieved calculable efficiency. From that triple start the way was clear. The pattern of development, from that time until 1900 was as follows.

1806: JOSEPH MANTON'S ELEVATING RIB

Joseph Manton (1795–1835) was probably the most inventive London gunmaker of the early nineteenth century; although he may not have been the greatest, as Colonel Peter Hawker insisted that he was. His elevating rib was simply a raising of the metal bar at the

Double-barrelled flint-lock gun by Joseph Manton made in 1807
The gunmaker Joseph Manton, with Henry Nock the greatest of the nineteenth-century innovators, introduced his elevating rib in 1806. The patent was designed to improve aim. Within fifty years Manton and his later contemporaries brought the shotgun from the age of the muzzleloader, a system which had remained static for two hundred years, into the modern age. Above all he evolved the game gun from a clumsy instrument into an arm of classic proportions.

chambers' end tapering off to the muzzle between the barrels of a double gun. It was widely acclaimed because it had the effect of correcting the common error of shooting low.

1800–1820: VINTAGE YEARS OF THE FLINT GUN

The two decades in which the London gunmakers, led by such as Joseph (1795–1853) and John Manton (1780–1834), Henry Nock (1772–1804), Durs Egg (1785–1834) and James Purdey the second (1784–1863) brought the flint gun to its highest degree of perfection. The essential shapes they arrived at are unchanged in breechloaders today.

1807: FIRST DETONATING LOCK

The invention of a Scottish clergyman, the Rev Alexander James Forsyth, which within a few years made the flint and steel method of ignition obsolete. A fulminate was exploded by the blow of a plunger which instantaneously fired the charge.

1813: FIRST GUN BARREL PROOF ACT

1816–1818: PELLET, CAP AND COPPER TUBE GUNS

Following Forsyth's patent, various detonating devices were developed, including Joseph Manton's percussion tube lock in 1818. The detonating system culminated in the universal use of copper caps mounted on a nipple.

1818–1820: DUAL LOCK SYSTEMS

Before copper caps were standardized to suit all guns, there was an interregnum in which weapons were designed to fire with flint and steel, percussion caps, and even Manton pellet-locks. A particularly confusing, but interesting, half-way house for the collector. Most conversions from flintlock to percusion proper were made in the next decade.

Pheasants—Types you can recognise

Four predominant strains of pheasant are normally immediately identifiable among the bag on a shooting day. None are pure bred. But four potent lines preserve in the cocks a recognisable plumage. Hens defeat the most ardent ornithologist. Others, like the golden pheasant, the Reeves and now the Versicolour, a Japanese bird, are rarities. These mounted specimens are in the collection of the Game Conservancy at Fordingbridge in Hampshire

Phasianus—A mongrel for all seasons

The Game Conservancy, who appropriately call him 'Charlie', selected this cock for mounting because he bears traces of all the common dominant types.

Phasianus mut. *tenebrosus*

Phasianus colchicus The Old English Blackneck

Phasianus torquatus

Joseph Manton's percussion tube lock

Hovering on the edge of new systems of ignition, Manton, ever inventive, introduced his tube lock, a refinement of the Forsyth patent of 1807. He did not live long enough to see the coming of the breechloader. He was criticised in his time; but if he got credit for an invention which was not altogether his own, posterity may well remember what another gunmaker said of him: 'But for him we should all be a parcel of blacksmiths'

In a period of swift change, Charles Jones's patent of 1833 is one of the hybrids, a muzzleloading percussion gun with the advantages of an enclosed detonating system. Described as a central fire muzzleloading double gun it had a transitional popularity. Jones was gunmaker to Prince Albert from 1825 to 1835. The external hammers, for cocking purposes only, are blind. The special feature is a thumb slide to waterproof the locks. The caps were placed on the nose of the hammers, and had the detonating composition outside on the crown of the cap, evidence of the variation of gun design through a generation

1818: INTRODUCTION OF DAMASCUS BARRELS

The gunmaker Rigby of Dublin, made the first 'Damascus' barrels; but they did not come into general use until after 1825. Prior to that, barrels were twisted out of horse shoe nail stubs. Damascus barrels (only remotely to do with the place called Damascus) were worked into their beautiful herring-bone patterns by the mingling of iron and steel. Even the new barrels were only reluctantly accepted by the old sportsmen.

1840's: NEEDLE AND PINFIRE ARMS

The last short phase before the standardization of the breechloader. The needle and the pin exploded the fulminate inside a cartridge.

1850: BEGINNING OF THE BREECHLOADER

The breechloader has earlier origins, but its definite phase was the introduction in France of LeFaucheux's drop-down action pinfire with a forward underlever below the fore-end. It was brought to London by the gunmaker Joseph Lang of Cockspur Street in 1851.

1852: FIRST CARTRIDGE EXTRACTING GUN

Charles Lancaster brought out a central fire underlever gun with extractors.

1858: BREECHLOADER ACCEPTED

Gun trials, organized by *The Field*, settled controversy about the merits, or otherwise, of the breechloading gun, which came into general use in the sixties. Stability in the design of hammer guns was achieved between 1866–1875.

1861: CENTRAL FIRE CARTRIDGES

The first true central fire cartridge in Britain was exhibited by Daw of Threadneedle Street at the Great Exhibition of that year.

1866: CHOKE BORING

The invention of the choke bore is generally attributed to Pape of Newcastle. W. W. Greener of Birmingham challenged it (1875).

1870: PURDEY'S BOLT ACTION

The son of Purdey the first brought out the familiar slide and top lever arrangement we know today.

1871: HAMMERLESS GUNS

Murcott of Haymarket, introduced the true hammerless gun ('Murcott's mouse trap').

1875: ANSON & DEELEY'S BOX LOCK ACTION

Two Birmingham craftsmen (of Westley Richards) introduced the simplest, cheapest and, with only four working parts, still one of the most reliable gun actions.

1875: SELF-EJECTING GUNS

Needham, a Birmingham gunsmith, produced the first mechanism to slip a fired cartridge out of a shotgun barrel. Frail and unreliable in the original invention, the system was perfected in the last decade of the century.

1878–1882: SMOKELESS POWDERS SUCCEEDED BLACK POWDER

1890: PROOF FOR SMOKELESS POWDERS (NITRO POWDERS) COMPULSORY

1900: QUICK RELIABLE SMOKELESS POWDERS

The birth of the breechloader

The French gunmaker LeFaucheux is attributed with the invention of the first successful breech-loader. Adopting the rimfire cartridge, he first marketed it on the continent in the eighteen-forties. It attracted no attention from the English gun trade until it was shown at the Great Exhibition in 1851. It was introduced in England, shortly afterwards by Joseph Lang

The central-fire gun. In 1852, Charles Lancaster invented the central-fire gun with extractors. Designed to shoot the original base-fire cartridge, the barrels move forward a short distance before dropping. An extended hook slides under the standing breech and the underlever closes the gun. Little was left to invent now except the true hammerless self-ejector.

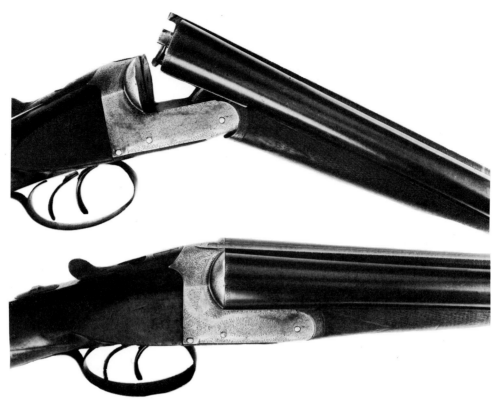

The first really successful hammerless gun

Anson and Deeley's boxlock (patent No 1756, May 1875) which emerged from Westley Richard's gun factory in Birmingham, is the stoutest gun action which has ever been devised. In early models, of the type illustrated here, the closure is not entirely satisfactory. But with subsequent improvements, the boxlock is certainly the best workaday gun

The boxlock, as it came to be called, gives quicker ignition and, with a strong mainspring and a quick hammer blow, introduced a mechanism which is still the most widely used gun action today. Sidelocks have better breeding. Boxlocks, with their simplicity of action, are working guns without parallel

One day in September, a Sabbath Morn,
I shot a hen pheasant, in standing corn,
Without a licence—'twas hard to plan
Such a series of crimes against God and man!

ANON. (1912)

CHAPTER 5

THE ETIQUETTE OF THE SHOOTING FIELD

It was between the two Great Exhibitions of 1851 and 1861, that a transformation came about in the English sporting scene which prevails to the present time. The breechloaders and the central fire cartridge became the normal gear of the shotgun sportsman. Although hammerless guns and smokeless powder were not wholly efficient for another twenty years a new code of conduct came into practice.

In 1885, Lord Walsingham and Sir Ralph Payne-Gallwey contributed to a series of sporting books named after the Duke of Beaufort's mansion at Badminton in Gloucestershire. They outlined the new system of driven game shooting. I say outlined because it was too early for them in a new technique to explore the secrets of straight shooting. Both in their day and in their way were deadly, but they could only partly explain why. Indeed, although other works appeared later it was not until after World War I that a sensible grammar of game gun shooting was first published. What Walsingham and Payne-Gallwey did, with notable success, was to establish etiquette and the principles of safety in the new sport.

Up to the time of Peter Hawker's death in 1853 it is questionable whether there was any shooting etiquette at all. 'Cockneys', as Hawker described them, popped off at any sitting bird with their calamitious gaspipes. Hawker himself has less than a clean record in the matter of modern sportsmanship. He made no bones that he chased partridges on horseback until they were too tired to lift off the ground. He used the vast cannon of punt guns to sweep a raft of duck off the surface of the water.

It is difficult to date exactly when organised shooting as it is managed today became accepted. It almost certainly had its origins in East Anglia, particularly in Norfolk and Suffolk where pheasants and partridges and almost every other game fowl flourish naturally in the marshy terrain. My own guess is that Thomas William Coke, son of Thomas Coke, the great agriculturist of eighteenth-century Norfolk, was certainly one of those who discovered the possibilities of driving game over guns rather than the old method of walking up behind dogs. (It is recorded in the Holkham, Norfolk Game Books that partridges were driven for the first time on January 5, 1875.) Under his management the bags of game shot at Holkham increased prodigiously. Under his formidable direction only the best shots had the courage to accept his invitation to his coverts. Any man who 'fluffed' his birds at Holkham was ordered home.

Even in the days of the detonating muzzleloaders, which fired almost as quickly as a breechloader today, sportsmen discovered that they could pull oncoming birds out of the sky. Although reloading was still a slow business a man with two guns and a servant could discharge four barrels in quick succession. With the introduction of the breechloader and the central fire cartridge, efficiency improved further. Smokeless powder finally cleared the view for the expert shots of the last quarter of the nineteenth century.

Early records exist of colossal bags of game taken by parties of minor royalty in middle Europe. Such 'battues' are not to be compared with the development of organised game-shooting in England. On the continent game was collected into a small area by armies of beaters and soldiers and hemmed in with nets. The shooters, undoubtedly aided by the sticks of the beaters and predictably not without risk to themselves and their attendants, entered the enclosure for a circus of slaughter.

In England the sport was elevated from a pot-hunting expedition to an art. Lines of beaters, with stops and checks, brought game over a line of numbered stands. The birds were managed, not to make it easier for the shooter, but by encouraging the quarry to fly tall and fast to test his marksmanship.

The first lesson was that there had to be rigid discipline when shooting in company. By the end of the nineteenth century the code of rules was firmly established. A man who swung his gun down the line was ordered off the field. Anyone who shot fur in front which might endanger the beaters, anyone who kept his gun loaded between stands and anyone who mangled a bird by shooting it at close range, was not 'the right sort'. An early edict was that, in a line of guns, a shooter should not poach birds flying straight to his neighbour. It was not done to appear at a shoot with brand new gear and new clothes. 'The right sort' was distinguished by well-worn tweeds and an old cartridge bag. It indicated that he had done it all before.

It was quoted as an example of the perfection of shooting etiquette that, when a covey of eight partridges was flushed between two famous shots, each of them killed two in front and, after changing guns, two behind, thus wiping out the covey. The feat was admired, not

PERFECTLY SAFE:
GUN BROKEN.

GUN ON SHOULDER:
CORRECT POSITION.

The Gent from Town.

because neither gun missed, but because each knew exactly which birds in the covey were properly in his own arc of fire.

The English tradition, from the start of modern gameshooting, has always been the strictest of any country in the world. People who offend are reprimanded by the captain of the shoot. It is a good system which has saved many accidents in a crowded country.

Today, it is also characterised by a happy, almost bantering relationship between guns and beaters. It is proper to add that it was not always so. Landowners, greedy for big bags, enforced punitive game protection laws. 'Moleskins', the gamekeeper (see Chapter 13), was regarded with fear and suspicion. Murder was not unknown in affrays between keepers and poachers in the pheasant coverts. In Victorian times, there were dark hints of mantraps. Gypsies used lurchers to drive hares into purse nets on their escape routes out of the fields. Until the Ground Game Act of 1880, tenant farmers were forbidden to kill the rabbits which plagued their land. Complicated laws, dating back to feudal times, bedevilled the relationship between 'the have's and the have-not's'. In periods of agricultural depression it was not surprising that countrymen were prepared to take considerable risks to poach the game which strutted and lolloped so invitingly just outside their cottage porches. The law could not easily warn off a man with an empty stomach and the taste, too, for 'a bit o' sport'.

The conservation of game by artificial methods came in the second half of the nineteenth century. Enterprising gamekeepers, anxious to increase their stock of birds, put clutches of pheasant eggs under broody hens. They quickly discovered that a higher proportion of penned chicks, protected from vermin, could be raised to maturity in greater certainty than if they had to take their chance in the wild. The eggs of the grey partridge were lifted from their nests, replaced with stone ones and only returned to the partridge hen when they were

59

The right sort   The wrong sort

chipping. The keepers also earned the unenviable reputation of shooting and trapping every form of fur and feather which they regarded as hostile to game. They boasted of their gibbets on which, in every wood, they exhibited the grisly remains of cats, hedgehogs and hawks, as well as more unlovable species, as a warning. In favoured areas the stock of game birds to the acre in Britain soon exceeded any other country in the world.

With the coming of the railways the privileged guns had the mobility to travel shooting estates from the beginning of the shooting season to its end. Their aim, and the aim of the landowners was to collect bigger and bigger bags, but slaughter to extinction was unwelcome.

The shooting calendar was organised as much to preserve as to destroy. At the beginning of September, if partridges were forward enough, the guns shot over the stubble, aiming to kill the leading birds in the covey (the old ones), and scatter the youngsters about the shoot. It ensured that a good stock of fertile young birds travelled to fresh fields instead of collecting in incestuous packs. In October, pheasants were shot on the 'outsides' of the estate so that they collected in the main coverts where they were fed, in time for the big shoots when the leaf was off the trees in November. After Christmas to the end of January, the rule usually was that only cock birds were shot. Because the pheasant is a polygamous bird it was established that it was not possible to shoot too many cocks. With a good stock of hens there were always enough male birds left to fertilise the eggs for the next season. A shooter who killed a hen on a 'cocks only' day blotted his copy book. It was like forgetting to tip the game keeper, or not sending a letter of thanks to your host for his invitation.

Grouse-shooting in Scotland, the most testing and exhilarating driven-game shooting of all, arrived later than it did in England. The Scots continued to shoot their muir-birds over pointers and setters. The red grouse is resistant to the domestication which suits the pheasant and, to a lesser extent, that squire of the English countryside, the grey partridge. But, before long, the Scots discovered—we may suppose with Sassenach help—that, by burning the old heather and encouraging the young shoots on whose bells the red grouse feeds, the population of a moor could be increased by tenfold, and more. From that time, the lairds discovered that the potential of profit from sporting rights was greater than any of their sheep-runs had hitherto afforded.

The top shots of Victorian times expected to fire ten-thousand rounds in a season. They used a pair or three matched guns by one of the best London makers and travelled the seasonal round of country houses with a skilled loader, and probably a valet as well. Most of them were titled landowners, but they expended all their vigorous prowess in shooting. Lord de Grey (later Marquis of Ripon) was counted 'one of the ten best shots in England', a man who could have three dead pheasants in the air at the same time, kill two partridges in front, change guns, and drop two behind. De Grey, who gave up keeping a detailed list of the game he killed after 1913, bagged 316,699 head between 1867–95, including 111,190 pheasants, 84,491 partridges, 47,468 grouse. Up to his death he brought his total score to well over half-a-million.

Contemporarily, it is considered rather bad form to add up a personal bag. I remember a good shoot in which our host asked us to write down on a scrap of paper what we each thought we had killed. A skilled shot, who was one of the guests, announced that he would not enter. 'When the score of the rest is added up,' he said, 'I expect that I will owe you a few.'

It is in fact rather odd that the Victorians and Edwardians made a practice, as they undoubtedly did, of calculating their personal bags. Sir Ralph Payne-Gallwey had a counter in the fore-end of his guns with which he could flick the score on as he was shooting. Today in the field it is considered improper to count, except perhaps privately. People here dislike the continental habit of issuing each gun with a card to record his contribution to the bag. Anyhow it depends on your picker-up ('valet' as he is euphemistically called in Spain) whether he has the fists and the legs to collect the game before the other fellow, and put it down to your name. The custom in England now is that only the total bag of all the guns is counted at the end of the day. I suspect that those Victorian shots were show-offs. In the pride of the Empire, they lacked a certain Anglo-Saxon restraint.

The enormous bags of game that were harvested each season were hampered to the markets to the great advantage of the thrifty housewife. As late as the season of 1939 before the phoney war ended, I recollect pheasants at six shillings and sixpence a brace in the poulterers' shops in December. The only loss was to the landowner's pocket. It used to be said of pheasant shooting that up goes a sovereign, the price of rearing it, bang goes twopence, then the price of a cartridge, and down comes half-a-crown. The figures were not quite accurate then. In these inflationary times, the cost of rearing a pheasant, the price of having the privilege to shoot it, and the value of one of the best of all gamebirds for the table has rocketed.

Not one has ever been wasted. Gameshooting, admittedly the sport of the rich, has constantly provided a valuable food crop for the table, as plentiful as the production of corn, roots and vegetables. More important, the rich have subsidised the harvest. It has always cost them more to shoot game than it cost them to eat it. The economics are the same today. In Victorian times it was also the province of the rich to spread their bounty, however much they persecuted the poacher who invaded their lands.

My mother told me that, in her girlhood, she remembered seeing Lord Rothschild's butler standing outside his town house at Hyde Park Corner to stop every horse omnibus which came by at Christmas, and present the driver with a brace of pheasants which he hung festively beside his box.

Oh yes, it was a feudal survival. Oh yes, the determination of the landowners to preserve their sporting rights is open to criticism. But the result was that wild birds came to be protected as they never had been before. Today in Britain the Royal Society for the Protection of Birds will prosecute you if you shoot anything much, apart from game, the crow family and, by local arrangement, song birds like bullfinches which threaten the fruit crops. The record is a proud one.

It is perhaps more questionable whether the huge bags which the Victorians and the Edwardians sought and achieved were justified. True, they supplied an important source of the food market. They created jobs for large numbers of country workers. Anyhow, they are a part of social history, the history of the shotgun.

King Edward VII, whose taste was impeccable and who always removed the band off his expensive Havana cigars so that nobody should be embarrassed by what he was smoking, had the last word. He is said to have remarked ruefully after a great day in the coverts when four thousand pheasants were killed:

'Aren't we overdoing it a bit?'

'The manufacture of firearms was not apparently one of the earlier British industries, and there was for long no guild, such as the Bowyers or Fletchers, to keep the special craft or mystery of the gunsmith's art.'

HUGH B. C. POLLARD

CHAPTER 6

THE MYSTERY OF GUNMAKING

A top engineer at the Rolls Royce works in Derby made a comment to me which has stayed in my memory. He said that there was nothing in a Rolls which was not also in the cars rolling off the mass-assembly lines. The difference, he explained, is that we throw out the parts which are below standard and, more important, we take much longer to put the bits together. It was a modest comment characteristic of a deprecating attitude, born out of pride, inherited from that guru of exquisite engineering, Sir Henry Royce, the founder of the firm. An exact parallel is the work committed to the building of a London Best gun.

It is correct that a modestly priced machine-made arm shoots just as far and as straight as a hand-made gun which costs thousands of pounds. It is not the gun, however enthusiastically the sportsman may insist on the hard-hitting qualities of his own weapon, but the propellant inside the cartridge which powers the shot charge. By way of comparison, a family car can largely be relied upon to deliver you to your destination. The classic car raises travel to a new dimension. A best gun raises shooting to just that.

The essential distinction between the ordinary and the extraordinary gun is the difference between a nappy old nag and a Thoroughbred horse, or between something you have picked up in the flea market and a custom-built instrument which has patiently been engineered for your personal needs. In competition over two hundred years the top London gunmakers have evolved a weapon which is at once an individual and a family heirloom.

It is individual because it is built to the measurements and taste of the owner, individual because every hand-made London gun has its own character recognisable at once by the

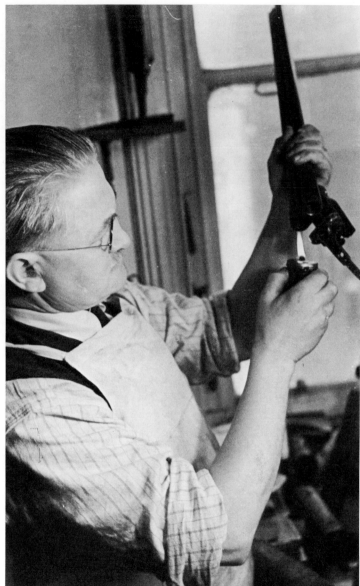

Master craftsmen—the old generation and the new

It was widely supposed in the middle of this century that the great craftsmen of the London gun trade were a disappearing race. The older generation of barrelmakers, stockers, actionmakers and finishers has indeed passed away. But a new younger breed has emerged and they are building guns as beautiful as any that were made in the past. The average age of the new men is in the thirties. The top London gun trade flourishes now as strongly as it has done for a hundred and fifty years.

craftsman who filed it. On the road with a Rolls Royce technician I recollect that he only had to glance at the number plates of one of his firm's cars to recall its history. If you call at Purdey's in South Audley Street in London's Mayfair today, they only need to know the number on the gun, anything from sixty to twenty-eight thousand. to tell you who bought it, the details of its measurements, the original choke in the barrels, and the precise date it was made.

Some of the makers were less lucky. Holland & Holland lost their detailed back records during the blitz in World War II. Robert Churchill's books, like Purdey's, are I believe, complete. But Churchill did not appear until the twentieth century. It is still remarkable that you can often trace the history of London Best guns more exactly than the geneaological trees of their owners. It is also notable that game books on the great shooting estates survive with details of the bags taken over a period of nearly two hundred years.

It is admonitory to add that not all London guns with great names on them like Purdey, Holland, Boss, Woodward, and the rest are still everything that they are cracked up to be. After generations even Best guns wear out.

It is not unknown for guns to be offered with great names on the ribs of the barrels and the sideplates to fool the unsuspecting. Forgers have assembled weapons, sometimes with engraved pieces out of muzzleloaders. If you decide to buy a second-hand weapon, whatever its apparent pedigree, let a gunmaker look at it first.

If you have the capital to acquire a new gun, or a pair, from one of the top makers you

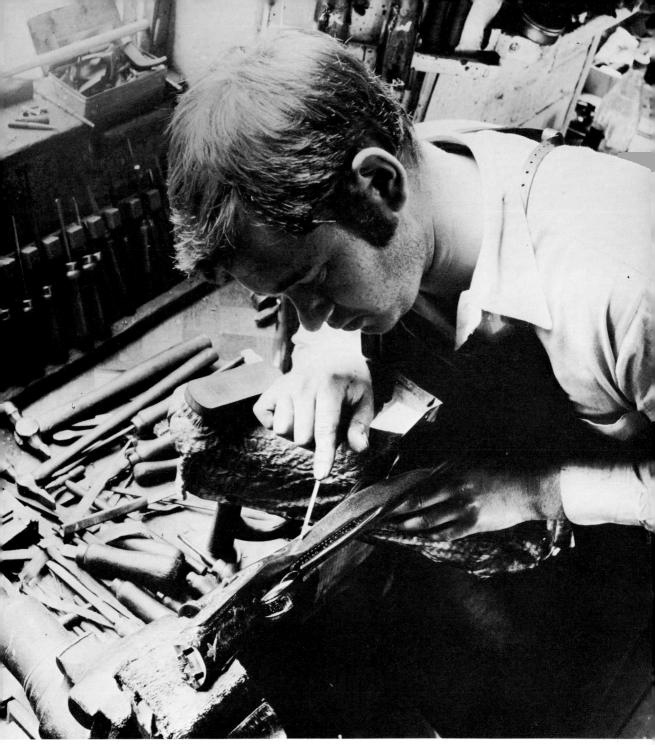

Mr John Richardson, one of the younger breed of stockers in the Holland & Holland factory, chequering the 16-bore gun of the 1968 set of five

may be sure that, whatever happens to the value of money, you have made a safe invest-ment. You will have to wait up to two years at the present for delivery. You will have to bide your time while the maker satisfies himself, in the shop and on his shooting grounds that he can fit you to suit all your own idiosyncrasies. He will probably submit you to a question-and-answer paper as detailed as an application for a life insurance policy.

What you will get, at the end of the line, is something as beautiful, and far more func-tional than anything every made by Fabergé. A mass-produced gun, which looks more or less as good as a Purdey when you take it out of the shop, will feel the strain after a few thousand rounds. The stock and the barrels will discolour. The actions will loosen. The trigger pulls will stiffen.

The difference between a hand-made weapon and the others is that a Best gun will shoot a hundred thousand rounds, and like it. The shot charge will pattern on target about 20 per cent better at a standard distance of 40yd. It will fit your shoulder and your arm as comfor-tably as a dogskin glove. It will probably be a pound lighter than a mass-produced gun. That is a factor which is a big element in a day's hard shooting. You may also depend on it that all the components of the gun will hug together in a sucking fit. The breech of a London Best gun will not close on a cigarette paper.

The muzzleloaders were much more individuals than the modern breechloaders. The old gunners had to experiment to discover the powder and shot charge which best suited individual arms. It is not so today.

Choke, a constriction of the barrels at the muzzle end of a gun, is no longer, as it used to be, an experimental business. It is not yet, nor perhaps ever will be, a science, but the pattern of shot from a charge at various ranges is now within a pellet or two, almost completely predictable.

In the past century, various bores of shotgun were fashionable, the word 'bore' indicating the number of lead balls fitting the barrels which added up to a pound. Wildfowlers like Colonel Peter Hawker, bruised their shoulders with 4-bores, 8-bores, and 10-bores. I believe that 28-bores are still favoured for small game by American sportsmen. Today the gun in most general use in all shotgun shooting is the 12-bore.

Contemporarily, only four bores of gun are regularly used in the English field; the 12, 16, 20 and the .410 (named after the barrel diameter). 'Sixteens', as they are called, are elderly men's or specialists' guns, 'twenties' are usually regarded as boys' guns, and 'four-tens' as vermin destroyers. Heavy wildfowl guns, except in the hands of hardy East Anglians on the saltings, are now largely obsolete. A short-barrelled magnum 12-bore, chambered for 2–in and 3in cartridges for wildfowl possibly points the way to the future.

In the mystery of gunmaking few subjects have caused more fiery debate than the length of shotgun barrels. Gervaise Markham, in the seventeenth century, recommended 6ft as the ideal length. With the ill-milled powder of his time, it might have helped. In Queen Anne's reign 42in was favoured. Generation after generation, shotgun barrels have steadily shor-tened. 36in dropped to 30in in the early days of the breechloaders.

In the first decade of the twentieth century, with the general adoption of nitro-proof powders, 28in barrels became the standard length. Most guns are still made to that measure-ment.

In the twenties came the 25in-barrelled guns which are now widely used in the field.

There was much controversy about them at the time. No doubt the length of gun barrels advocated by our forefathers was excessive. At 32in and over there is a downward flip in the metal of the tubes which encourages the common fault of shooting behind a moving target. At 25in there is an upward flip in the metal. The gun, because of its shorter length, lifts quicker on to the target, especially in covert, but it makes a recognisable crack on discharge and, undoubtedly, especially in hands inexperienced in taking recoil it has a sharper kick. When the 25in guns were first introduced, it was also said that there was a loss in the velocity of the charge. So there is, but it is negligible. Almost all game is shot well within the limits of any gun, whatever its barrel length.

The vast majority of shotguns built in London today have barrels of 28in which experience has shown have neither a downward nor an upward flip. Aesthetically a tall man looks better, and possibly shoots better, with barrels of that length. Although I am a six-footer I have shot, not badly, with 25in guns all my sporting life.

Although the inventiveness of the London gun trade vastly increased during the nineteenth century, it has since settled into a strictly conservative tradition. Personally, I cannot see why it should not. Nothing more is wanted from it which is not well within the limits of the present gun's capacity.

The conservatism is expressed in the way that sportsmen still generally prefer to shoot with what are called sidelocks. The gunmakers prefer to make them. Sidelocks are simply weapons in which the hammers, instead of showing on the outside of the gun, are enclosed behind the action plates. The weapon has an altogether more graceful appearance. It is arguable that the balance is better, that the weight of the gun falls more sweetly into the shooter's hands. Yet the fact of the matter is that the most remarkable improvement in shotgun design was achieved by two Birmingham craftsmen in 1875. With only four working parts, Anson and Deeley's boxlock action is the safest, most reliable and foolproof ever devised. It is normally incorporated in medium-priced guns. Travelling the world, I have learnt that an A & D boxlock is the most foolproof gun you can carry.

The invention of the A & D hammerless action, now familiarly known as a boxlock, revolutionised the gun and its mode of operation. John Deeley (1825–1912) subsequently became the chairman of the Westley Richards company. He himself modestly insisted that the working design was Anson's. It reduced the number of parts in an action by no fewer than fifteen.

In *Modern Sporting Gunnery* (1906), Dr Henry Sharp wrote that 'It saved the sportsman thought and trouble, increased the speed of loading and firing . . . and removed one of the causes of accident inseparable from the gun with external hammers.' With minor modifications it has not been essentially improved since.

A few A & D's have been built of London Best quality. They are now among the most sought-after weapons in the second-hand market. Light guns weighing as little as 5¾lb with 25in barrels; they are collectors' pieces.

In assessing the importance of shotguns as collectors' weapons, apart from their use in the field, it is valuable to discount what the gunmakers' themselves call 'gingerbread', the gold ornament and engraving put on to make the weapon look prettier to the eye. To the inexperienced, a shotgun looks the richer if the action plates are engraved with pictures of game birds; if the barrels, or even the triggers, are gilded.

The over-and-under gun

By comparison with the graceful side-by-side barrels which are preferred in the shooting field in Britain, the over-and-under gun, much as it is admired on the continent, appears clumsy. Beautiful weapons are built, like these, with deep engraving, but they do not look quite right in the autumnal coverts nor match in with the disciplined discretion of a quieter scene

It is the cheapest bit of work which is applied. The more decoration you find (continental guns are particularly prone to it), the more suspicious you should be that it may be concealing defects in craftsmanship. The most discreet looking arms with only fine scroll engraving on the action plates, are the aristocrats. The engraving on them serves a purpose. It softens the face of the gun metal which might otherwise turn game by flashing like a heliograph in the field.

Over the years all manner of improvements have been devised. The single-trigger gun has enjoyed limited success. It is a help to shooters with a bad grip who are inclined to bruise a finger on recoil. But most, I think rightly, prefer guns with two triggers under the guard controlling right and left barrels. They are more flexible and they are less liable, if only fractionally, to mechanical defect.

Different makers have modifications which they introduce into their own actions. Provenly, the most famous is the Purdey action. Patented in 1880 by Mr Beesley, who later set up business on his own account, it has a double spring of different strengths. The upper arm cocks the tumbler on opening. The less powerful spring is used for rotating the tumbler in the firing of the gun.

Others among the top makers have refinements of their own. Not the least is a detachable lock which can be lifted out of the gun in the way you can unscrew the lock of a muzzle-loader. I am not at all sure that the service is valuable. Wise sportsmen leave the care of the actions of their guns to their makers. Anyhow, I have never discovered that there is any true advantage of one action by a great maker over another. Filed with affection, few of them go wrong.

Over-and-under guns, the two barrels soldered together vertically, not horizontally, are widely used on the mainland of Europe. They are also popular with Americans for their national game of clay-pigeon shooting called 'skeet'. Those built in London are largely for export. O & U's have never really caught on in Britain where shooting men feel that the conventional gun handles more sweetly. It is a matter of taste.

At the beginning of this chapter I quoted an engineer at Rolls Royce who also said to me that the Americans could build as good a car tomorrow if they had the patience to resist the hustle implicit in the national phrase 'let's go'. London Best guns are what they are because the makers insist that the buyers must wait. Hurry is the enemy of fine craftsmanship. The Americans, who manufacture superb rifled weapons, have no proof houses to test barrels under stress conditions as we have in London and Birmingham. Individual firms proof their own weapons. But, because there is no authority to permit finesse in the reduction of weight, the American shotgun is heavier and over-metalled.

It is also a matter of national characteristics. An apprenticeship in the London gun trade is five years. It used to be seven before the school leaving age was raised. It was once thought that the trade would die as the average age of the old craftsmen climbed. It does not look like it now. Young men who start learning their trade by filing their own turnscrews out of the hardened steel of old gunsprings, are now building guns as good as any which were made in the past. The heritage is still a living one, although it is sad that the numbers of independent gunmakers decreases year by year.

'The gunmaker is something of a multiple personality at the best of times, for, in point of fact, an arm is seldom made by any one man. It is the work of barrel maker, lock maker, spring maker, stocker, mounter, engraver and even more specialists. The gunmaker himself was usually one who had served an apprenticeship to the trade and knew how to execute most of the work of the various departments and how to finish and repair the complete weapon. He was, in a word, the master craftsman who supervised the whole and often put the finishing touches, but it is a mistake to regard an arm as the handwork of an individual. It should be looked on as the work of his particular school or shopful of skilled craftsmen.'

HUGH B. C. POLLARD

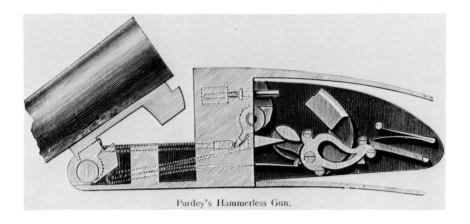

Purdey's Hammerless Gun.

CHAPTER 7

LOCK, STOCK AND BARREL

Far away from the gunshops, among the stands of walnut trees in the valley of the Dordogne in south-western France, the land of *huile de noix* and *pâté de foie gras*, the timber is growing which a generation hence will provide beautifully figured stocks for London Best guns.

In the city of Liège in Belgium rather special smiths are tubing close-grained steel which will ultimately be worked into barrels for a pair of guns for somebody who I trust is worthy to carry them. The forgings, I am told, are imported from Austria.

At first acquaintance it is a little surprising to learn that the raw materials of an English handmade gun may be of foreign origin. It is a tradition hallowed by history. In the Middle Ages the Plantagenet King Edward III made a wise enactment that for every hogshead of wine shipped into the country from the continent a protective tariff would be imposed of six yew staves. Although it is legendarily supposed that the yews in English village church-yards were planted to provide archers with their longbows, English yew was not straight-grained enough for a good bow. The trees in churchyards, whose foliage is poisonous to cattle, were planted there to make the farmers fence off their stock from holy ground. Similarly, English walnut is no better for gunstocks than English yew was for bows.

It may appear more puzzling that the London makers go to Belgium for their rough tubes. The Belgian arms manufacturers are more largely known today for the production of machine-made weapons at the cheaper end of the market; although they are still respected for superior arms. It is well to remember that, for hundreds of years, the continental smiths fashioned the best twist-barrels. At the turn of the century Whitworth fluid steel, made in England, superseded them. But, at the end of the line, Vulcans in small forges in the main-land of Europe are geared to the art of making high-grade steel tubes, clear of impurities, which are unequalled anywhere else in the world.

The rough walnut blank shown alongside a finished gunstock

I cannot tell you where to find them. I cannot tell you where, in the Dordogne, you might buy the blocks of walnut which, ten, twenty, thirty years hence, will be carved into gunstocks. The gunmakers will not reveal it to you, nor even to each other. The dark secrets of the trade are still carefully concealed. London gunmakers boast that they do not know what their competitors are up to.

Most gunmakers today buy tubes, from the mystery place where they happen to find them, which they work into finished barrels. An exception is Holland & Holland which I believe is one of the last firms today to engineer Vicker's forgings into finished barrels.

The magic begins when they have collected the rusty tubes which have satisfied them, the rough blocks of walnut wood which they store away for decades, like squirrels, in their workshops. In the past, the craftsmen filed guns in the shop windows to attract custom. In my own lifetime, I recollect seeing saddlers in the Haymarket stitching leather. Almost all the craftsmen have gone away now from the West End of London to the suburbs. London has lost something. To my knowledge only the cobblers of Lobb's the bootmakers, still pursue their craft in the eighteenth-century shop in St James's. It is a matter of rents.

For the making of a London Best gun the rough metal and wood calls for the workmanship of at least a dozen skilled craftsmen. There is the barrelmaker, the actionmaker, the lock filer, the stocker, the engraver, the mounter, the finisher. There are those who at various stages in the building of the gun pattern the performance of the weapon at targets. Finally there are those who make the lovely leather and wooden cases in which they are enclosed.

I have encountered only one man in my life who, with his own hands, can lock, stock and barrel a London Best gun. In any age, such a craftsman must have been rare. Now in his eighty-first year, Mr Harry Lawrence, for long the managing director of James Purdey

74

Mr C. Harry Lawrence with one of a pair of two dummy guns he built for Queen Mary's Doll's House at Windsor in the early twenties. The barrels were $3\frac{1}{2}$in long

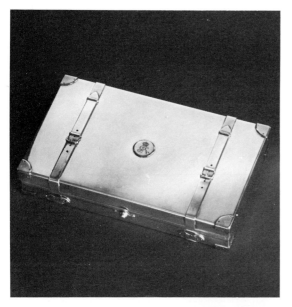
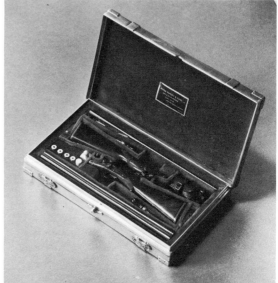
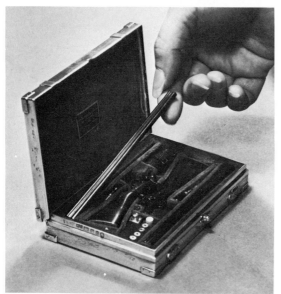
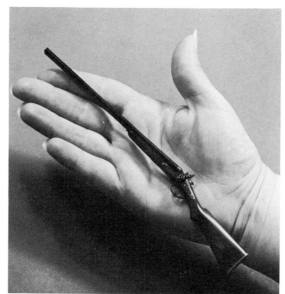

'This pair of guns is one sixth the size Your Majesty uses'
A presentation in a silver case by Garrard the jewellers, from the gunmakers Messrs Purdey & Sons
to King George V on the occasion of his Silver Jubilee. The guns, miniature replicas of the hammer
guns which the king used, even fire an appropriate cartridge. 7½in long, the pair is now in the
royal collection at Sandringham. The guns are numbered in Purdey's records 25000 and 25001.
The numbers also appear on the three components of the guns themselves, but you would need a
magnifying glass to read them

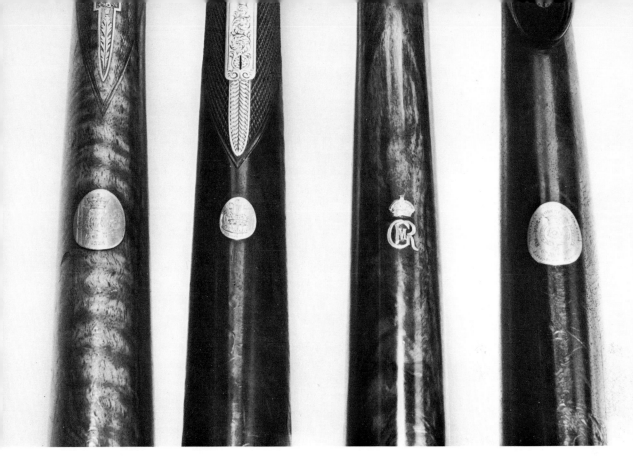

Monograms on royal gun butts
(*Left to right*) A gift from HRH the Prince of Wales to HRH the Duke of Clarence on his 21st Birthday, January 8, 1885; the crest of the Prince of Wales (King Edward VII); the royal cypher of George VI; one of the set of three presentation guns given by the townspeople of King's Lynn (Alfred Ream, Mayor) to the Duke of York on his marriage in 1893. The gold plate on the Purdey guns is still decipherable

and Sons, is numbered among the immortals of his trade, if only because it was he who inspired the miniature pair of guns, $3\frac{3}{4}$in long, for Queen Mary's Doll's House at Windsor. And he did better than that. For King George V he made another pair of matching Lilliputian guns, $7\frac{1}{2}$in long, which actually fire an appropriately sized cartridge. They are in the Royal Collection at Sandringham.

It is important to recognise that the London Best gun is fitted to a nicety for its original owner. Any taste he may have for choke boring, grip on the stock, style of forehand, or even engraving, is custom-built. Even in a matched pair of guns the barrels and forehand of number one won't marry into number two. There is admittedly a little bit of luck that the figuring in the walnut stocks may be more beautiful in one pair of weapons than others. But Best gun is as much a person as craft can make it.

The heart of the gun is in the barrels. Side by side, or over and under, they appear to be parallel. They are not. They are brazed together at a convergent angle so that at a mean distance of 40yd the shot charge from both barrels centres on the target. At lesser ranges, at which most game is taken, the margin of the shot pattern is sufficient in width, as well as in depth, for all practical purposes. The length of the barrels, which has been argued about for a century is relatively unimportant.

The most significant aspect in barrel-making is choke. If a gun has been designed for a certain barrel length you cannot chop off a few inches without destroying its performance. The reason is that the barrels of good guns are not cylinders. They are reasonably loose in the chambers, maybe two-thousandths of an inch to admit the cartridge, and tighter in the muzzle according to taste to regulate the pattern of shot. Choke varies from full choke to cylinder; or more usually these days what is called 'improved cylinder'.

It is remarkable that despite all the advances in engineering, nobody has yet found a more satisfactory way to make barrels which are better than those made by the appraisal of the human eye. When the rough tubes come into the gunshop, probably not straight and true, it is only the barrelmaker, picking out the shadows in the line of the metal, who can discover the faults. There are instruments which measure the tubes every three inches. But, at the end of the line, a human glance is the most precise instrument of all.

The same is true in the fashioning of the actions. I have heard it said that machines can marry two or even three surfaces. The actioners of a Best gun expect to file half-a-dozen working parts into a sucking fit. It is a laborious business. They use lamp black as they put the gun together. If they find the slightest disturbance in the soot on the faces of the metal parts they work on them again. It is not until there is not the slightest friction in the moving elements of the gun that it is accepted. It is notable that the springs in Best guns are so beautifully tempered that they survive under pressure for a hundred years, and more.

I doubt whether there is any mechanical skill which equals the love put into a Best gun. It is arguable that the effort is wasted. An artifact of the chase scarcely deserves it. Yet, as the poet Keats argued, 'beauty is truth, truth is beauty.' I am inclined to think that not since the fifth century BC has anything been made functionally better than a London Best gun. You need not shoot it. Just look at the lovely thing it is. Hundreds of years hence, collectors will cosset this production of our age.

Nothing is more hazardous in the creation of the gun than the working of the stocks and the fore-ends. Metal can be disciplined. Wood is unpredictable. In the past all sorts of woods were tried for stocks. Maple, because of its lovely figuring, was for a time favoured. But it is too brittle. Over the years, walnut has proved that it is the hard wood, with a beauty of figure equal to any wood in the world, which is incomparable for gunstocks.

Seasoning the rough stocks is a gamble. They lie in the timber yards and season in the gunmakers' shops, for a generation. The stockmakers measure them and match them as best they can for a pair of guns. When they carve them out there is always the chance that they will find a 'shake', a fault developed in the wood when it was swept as a sapling by the wind. It has to be thrown away. The selection of walnut wood for a gunstock is ruthless. Those that survive, last. The best, especially a pair of figured stocks which compare perfectly, are the masterpieces of the gunmaker's art.

The sportsman is unlikely to be concerned with the months of labour in the workshops

(*Opposite*) Shapes of gun stocks

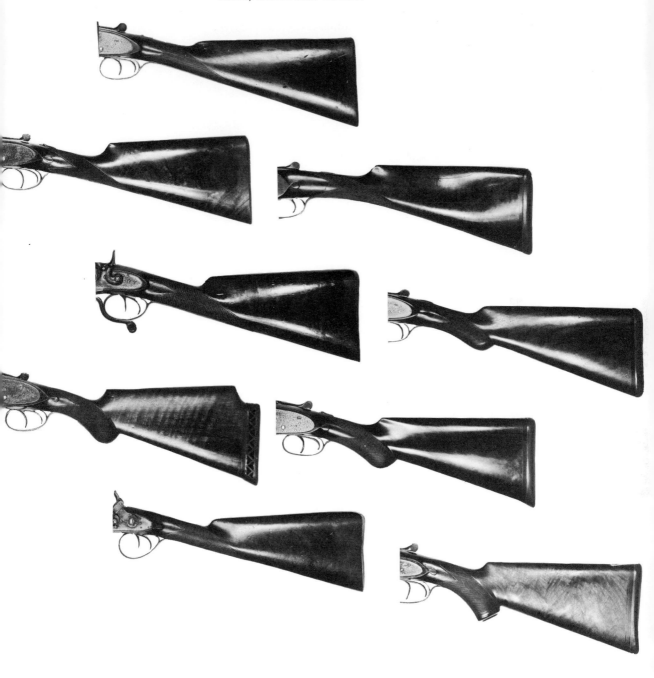

which put a gun into his hands. But it is as well to appreciate what went into it. It has been said that the most selective man should shoot his guns 'in the white' before they have been case-hardened and blued. But, in any event, he should make his own decisions. There are many factors which are a matter of individual choice. Choke comes first. It is a matter of considerable personal concern to every owner of a gun. Very many shooting men have only the vaguest notion of the effect of choke in actual practice.

Here is a table, based on a 12-bore gun with a standard cartridge, to assist:

Super choke:	75 per cent or 225 pellets of a 300 pellet charge within a 30in circle at 40 yards.
Full choke:	70 per cent or 210 pellets within a 30in circle at 40 yards.
Three-quarter choke:	65 per cent or 195 pellets within a 30in circle at 40 yards.
Half choke:	60 per cent or 180 pellets within a 30in circle at 40 yards.
Quarter choke:	Should put 50 per cent of pellets or 150 pellets into a 30in circle at 40 yards.
True cylinder:	40 per cent of pellets or 120 pellets into a 30in circle at 40 yards.

From that table do not suppose that the super choke, which puts the greatest number of pellets into a 30in circle, is the best barrel for you. It is very unlikely indeed that it is. But, if you are investing in a new gun, and deciding how much choke you think you will need, it is just as well if you have the slightest doubt, to err by having too much choke rather than too little. Later, you can ask the gunmaker to bore it to a larger size. Broadly, apart from a wildfowling gun, you may do best with improved cylinder in the right barrel and half choke in the left. In practice I am bound to say that the subtlety even then will not make much difference to your performance in the field.

The shooter is more likely to be affected by the shape of the stock and the fore-end, and the weight of the trigger pulls. The gunmaker may be relied upon to set up a stock to suit your shoulder. The great Joseph Manton established a shape for a stock which has not been improved. While there are variations which are accepted for different forms of shooting, the essential pattern of Manton's design is unchanged.

It is arguable that the fore-end, the third limb of the gun which locks the barrels to the stock and provides the spring which ejects the expended cartridges, is the one part of a modern game gun which has not been perfected. It is surprising that the choice of a fore-end offers such a variety, from the American beaver-tail, as it is called, to the hump-backed and raised fore-end which some trap shots prefer. Some clever gun craftsman may well improve on what has been achieved so far.

At present it appears that the fore-end should not be too smooth of surface. It is very important that the hand of the shooter should not slip. On the other hand the checkering must not be too rough to injure or bruise the hand on recoil. In addition it is important that it ought to be a non-conductor of heat so that a great number of rounds can be shot quickly without discomfort. On aesthetic grounds, it ought not to be too large or conspicuous and it ought to be at least as light as the standard fore-end which is in use on game guns now. The tradition of the English trade is to keep down any overweight in the gun.

On balance, the nearest the gunmakers have got to the solution of the problem is the

Various old styles of boring
1 True cylinder   2 'Relief' boring   3 Ordinary cylinder

Various choke-bores
4 Recess Choke   5 Recess Choke in Choked Barrel   6 True Choke

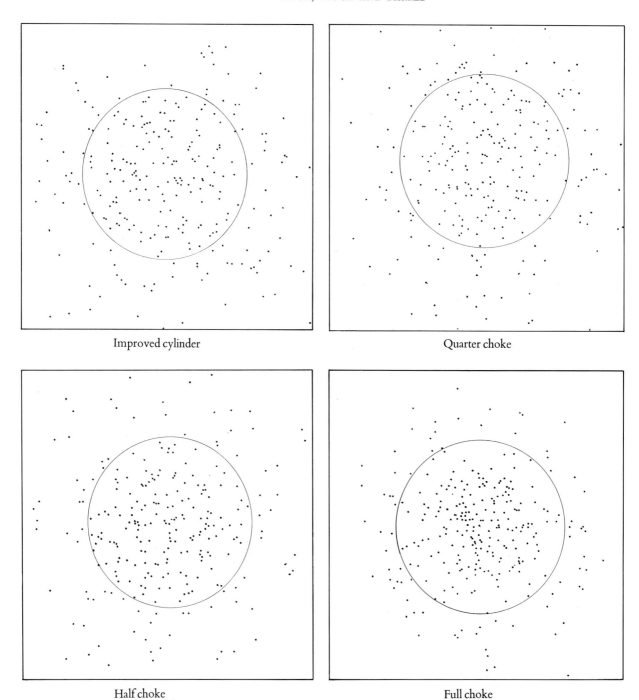

Improved cylinder

Quarter choke

Half choke

Full choke

(Opposite) **A tableau of shotgun patterns**
The data represent the average pattern performance of 12-bore game guns (based on a 30in circle and a range of 40yd) using different degrees of barrel choke. The cartridges were the standard Eley Grand Prix loaded with $1\frac{1}{16}$oz of No 6 shot. Charges were 287–289 pellets. Shooting at pattern testing plates produced the following pellet counts within the 30in circle:

Improved cylinder	147	=	51%
Quarter choke	158	=	55%
Half choke	174	=	61%
Full choke	199	=	69%

These representations have been painstakingly made for me by the experts at Eley directly from photographs of patterns thrown by cartridges taken at random from a production loading machine. The actual photographs, when reproduced to book size, would not have provided sufficient clarity to allow a ready appreciation by the reader. However, by pin piercing each pellet mark a stencil was obtained from which a clear print was made.

The patterns illustrated are those of the most commonly used load in 12-bore guns. It is evident that shot charges for guns with other loads, other shot sizes and other bores will show relative variations. But, these days, they will be consistent.

It is important to recognise that not all the pellets hit the pattern plate with equal striking energy. A shot charge in flight is a column of pellets which has depth as well as diameter. The charge fans out progressively, yard by yard, after leaving the barrel. The pellet energy at impact cannot be assessed from pattern tests.

The connoisseur is recommended to study the tables in the appendices. Fractional variations in the count of shot occur in the cartridges. If your gun is an old one, wear may have reduced the performance of choke. But it is plain, looking at the patterns on these pages, that if you shoot straight you will not miss much, however constricted the choke, or lack of it.

leather handguard with a fastener to fix it in place. The ordinary handguard, which is a metal sheath encased in leather, is a most beneficial accessory which can be fitted to the barrels of any gun.

The leather handguard has three advantages:
(1) It improves the variability of the hand grip on the fore-end considerably.
(2) It effectively protects the hands from heated barrels when a great many rounds have been shot in quick succession.
(3) It provides a warm and pleasant grip in hard weather when the metal of the barrels becomes almost as uncomfortably cold as in hard shooting it becomes uncomfortably hot.

The objection to the handguard, if it is merely sprung over the fore-end, is that it has a dangerous habit of slipping on recoil. Clearly the wisest course is to get the gunmaker to lock it into place.

In drooling as I have over the London Best gun, I must admit that the need for a leather handguard is an admission of weakness. After a lifetime of shooting, the fore-end is the one part of a London gun which another Joseph Manton might improve. As 'Capability' Brown, the eighteenth-century landscape gardener would have said: 'There are capabilities here.' I sincerely hope that the London gunmakers and their craftsmen are not too conservative to attempt it.

By comparison, trigger pulls are an eclectic interest. Back yard guns, indeed the sort of gas pipes which are normally exhibited in murder trials, have trigger pulls which are alarmingly tough. In one notorious murder trial in which the great King's Counsel Sir Patrick Hastings was defending his client Mrs Elvira Barney, who was accused of shooting her homosexual lover, he successfully defeated the prosecution by demonstrating in court, against Robert Churchill's expert evidence, how easy it might be for the gun to go off by accident. Years later, in his autobiography, Sir Patrick revealed that he bruised his trigger finger so badly pulling the trigger that it did not recover for a week.

In a machine-made gun precise trigger pulls are more than you can ask for your money. In a London Best they can be controlled exactly. If you are not a very keen shooting man indeed it is possible that it has never occurred to you that the trigger pulls, or the shape of triggers and trigger guards, should be a matter of any significance. First class shots can become so sensitive about the trigger pulls of their guns that they can notice a difference of half a pound or less. The weight of trigger pull depends on the weight of the gun.

A coach at a shooting school put it to me like this:

'If you are one of those sensitive shots accustomed to put on exactly the same amount of pressure every time you fire, you will probably require that your 6½lb guns should have pulls of 3lb right trigger and 3¾lb left trigger. But if you use a lighter 12-bore, or even a 20-bore weighing perhaps only 5½lb, you will find that, although the lighter weapon may have exactly the same measurements as your heavier gun, the pull you require will have to be altered. As a rough guide, the weight of the first or right trigger pull should be approximately one-half the weight of the gun. A 6lb pull on a 13lb 8-bore feels just as light as a 3lb pull on a 12-bore of 6½lb or a 2½lb pull on a 20-bore weighing 5lb. Generally speaking, the left pull should always be about 25 per cent heavier than the right because the greater leverage makes it feel proportionately lighter.'

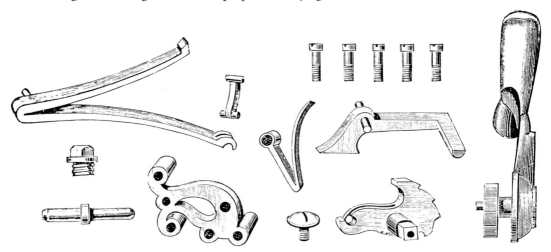

Pieces of a hammer gun lock

Phasianus c. mongolicus

The English partridge with the horseshoe
on his breast is a native

The redleg, Frenchman or Hungarian partridge is an immigrant, a heavier more showy bird than
the grey partridge and with rather different habits. He is not a true partridge at all. The two species
do not interbreed

Charles Tunnicliffe was never a sporting artist. He illustrated birds, like this raft of mallard, without a man with a gun in sight. Indeed, he shot birds with his brush and his pencil

The gunners who shot live pigeons out of traps used incredibly light pulls. A practitioner told me that he used a gun with a 1¾lb right pressure. As there was no safety catch on the gun, he had to be very careful indeed, when he closed it, that it did not go off by accident. Latterly, he used a 2¼lb pull on a 6lb gun. I cannot recommend it to the ordinary sportsman. Far better, I think, to have a heavy pull. Many good shots prefer it.

You should judge your gun, not by the weight of its pull, but by its crispness. The best lock always gives a never varying safe-and-sound pull. The cheap lock, owing to the irregularities of its component parts, cannot fail to vary; further, the shaping of the sears and the bent of the tumblers is cruder and only too often the pull is a long drag. Good guns do not require that triggers be pulled. The triggers are just touched as the gun is settled into the shoulder.

Not the least of the arts of lock, stock and barrel is the balance of weight. A Best gun is largely the thing that it is because every little fault in an ounce of walnut stock, every two-thousandths of an inch in the metal of the action, is carefully eliminated. *The stocks are balanced by reducing the weight with bore holes.* Ounces are important. At the end of the line, the gun must lift good and true at the end of a man's arm.

The perfect gun should be an extension of the shooter's pointing finger. In practice, none of us are perfect and the shooter has his off-days. If it were not so, it would not be worth going shooting. Missing is why we all try again.

It is evident that few of us are likely to have guns built for our own physical shape. Many are inherited. If you are lucky enough to inherit much of the same characteristics as your forbears, guns may fit. Unless you are left-handed or cross-eyed, the probability is that the gunmaker can vary the length and angle of the stock to suit you, although it is likely to be expensive. The comfort is that, in young hands especially, a good gun, within the wide margin of its shot charge will shoot reasonably well for you.

Older men, who have changes of eye, are likely to find that they are off-target, even with guns that fitted them in the past like gloves. Going to shooting school can put the matter right, even without alteration in gunstocks. You just have to modify the way you look at the target. It is a pity to alter a pair of guns in admission of old age. If you know what you are doing you can shoot just as well as you did in the past.

(*Opposite*)

Parts of a game gun: barrels

1 Foresight   2 Top Rib   3 Extractors   4 Keel Rib   5 Rear Lump   6 Forward Lump   7 Hook
8 Fore-end Loop   9 Bottom Rib   10 Flats Showing Proof Marks   11 Chambers

Stock and action

12 Cocking Levers   13 Extractor Cam   14 Comb   15 Action Face   16 Striker Holes   17 Top
Lever   18 Top Strap or Tang   19 Safety Slide   20 Knuckle   21 Lockplate   22 Triggers
23 Trigger Guard   24 Chequering   25 Heel   26 Screws (called Pins by Gunmakers)   27 Toe

Fore-end

28 Ejector Kickers   29 Chequering   30 Fore-end Diamond   31 Fore-end Tip   32 Release Button

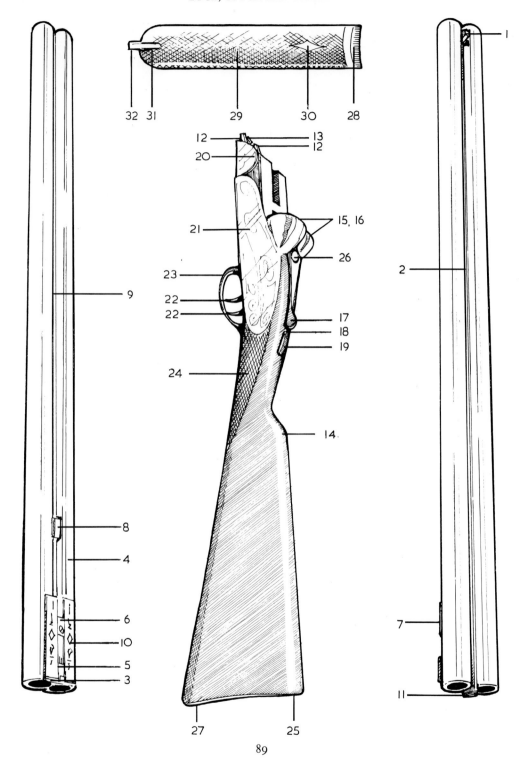

'The fitting of the stock of a gun to an individual is one of the highest arts of gunmaking. The length of stock necessary depends not only on the length of the shooter's arms, the breadth of his body and the length of his neck, it also depends on the position of the left hand, the position of stance and finally the weight of the gun.'

ROBERT CHURCHILL

CHAPTER 8

THE FINESSE OF
GUNFITTING

Looking at small arms up to the middle of the seventeenth century, with their clumsy stocks, it is impossible to regard them as other than lethal fireworks. It is not until the end of the eighteenth century that they emerged in a shape in which fairly accurate shooting was possible.

The techniques of gunfitting and game gun shooting can be extended little more than one hundred years. It is reasonable to think of it as three or, at most, four generations of lifetimes.

At the tail end of the eighteenth century, the gunmaker Henry Nock built the first guns with a roach-bellied stock which still looks good to the modern eye. The brothers Manton, and then Purdey, followed him with the square gunstocks with a deep toe which are still widely admired. The style of accurate gunfitting emerged a mere century ago.

Even now it is not a precise art. Much of it is pragmatic. Much still depends on the ocular skill of the gunfitter. Like the cutter in a tailor's shop, some are better than others. A first class gunfit is what you pay for. In a bespoke gun the margin of error is reduced because the pattern of shot, in a column which has depth as well as diameter, makes allowance for errors of judgement. It is nevertheless precautionary to add that a gun which fits you like a glove when you are thirty years old may fall off target at sixty when muscles stiffen, eyes change,

Gunfitting at the London shop of Purdey & Son

and footwork is not so secure. The gunmakers can do something about it, or even show you how to correct a fault of age in your gun-aiming. He has his methods.

If you have ordered a shotgun to be built for you the first step in arriving at your idio-syncratic style is a test which, without benefit of a gunfitter, you may experiment with yourself. Making sure that your gun is empty, get a friend to hold the tip of his index finger on the level with his eye. Mount your gun to point at it. If you point to right or left, above or below, on first aim, the gun does not fit you.

The gunfitter uses that device as his first check. The next stage is setting his try-gun. The try-gun is a weapon of measurement in which, with a key, the stock can be lengthened, raised or lowered, cast-on or cast-off to right or left. The shooter fires at the tin silhouettes of

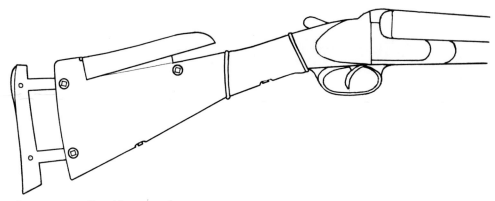

The try-gun or adjustable gun stock

birds swinging in front of whitewashed plates. When he is off-target, the gunfitter adjusts the try-gun until, at a fixed range, the shooter is on the bull.

It is necessary to add that nothing defies the skill of the fitter more than a man whose mounting, gunfitting and footwork is 'all over the place'. The first essential is the correct drill for gun-mounting, trigger-pressing, and that vital thrust of the shoulder into the butt of the gun (see Chapter 14). The gunfitter is looking for *consistent* mistakes. With variations of his try-gun he knows how to correct them.

The next phase in gunfitting is shooting at clays in the shooting school. One of the secrets of gun coaches is that they read the pattern of your shot as you fire at a moving clay target. At first it appears a mysterious gift. In fact any average shot, by taking a bit of trouble, can acquire the skill himself. The method, once again with a friend, is to bend or kneel down behind him, directly in line with his gun barrels as he shoots. At first you will see nothing. But, preferably on an overcast day, you can train your eye to see what the gun coaches see, a disturbance in the air about the target, a sort of dark puff which will tell you whether he is in front or behind, above or below.

With practice an experienced shot judging not by movement in the air, which he cannot and should not see if he has his eye on the target, can learn to assess his own mistakes in gun drill. 'I was off balance.' 'I hesitated in my trigger-pressing.' 'I was behind him.' 'I was over the top.' Once you achieve that you may not be a great shot but you will always be a reliable one.

It is an illusion, which many have hopefully believed, that you can find out why you miss by using 'tracer' cartridges. These leave a rocket trail in the air behind the charge. They are delusory because the shot charge travels so much faster than the rocket. If you have 'killed' a moving target the tracer will be yards behind. You will do best not to bother with them.

Not the least of the problems in gunfitting is the choice of stock. Specialists, especially trap-shots and skeet shots, favour gunstocks in eclectic shapes. Most sportsmen who go to the top shotgun makers are content, and rightly so, to leave the matter to the people who, generally speaking, know best what you are going to shoot best with. The pistol grip, which some men prefer, can be produced as a quarter, a third or full grip. It is said in its various degrees to be more suitable for single-trigger guns. I have always thought—it may be a personal prejudice—that pistol grips are unsuitable for ordinary driven game shooting.

I prefer the style, which Joseph Manton pioneered, of the square deep-toed stock. I, for one, am more thrilled by a pair of perfectly matched mahogany stocks—I admit to a taste for those figured in beautifully veined pale colours—than I am for any variation in the classic shape. I am convinced that I will shoot better with them; and I will.

The gunmakers can bend the hardwood of walnut into incredible shapes. One-armed men, cross-eyed men, can be accommodated with guns which will serve their personal needs. I yield to no one in my admiration of what can be achieved. But it always worries me, in the top gunshops, to see beautiful things which have to be modified to meet unusual circumstances. Those of us who fit into the common line are lucky.

Although I have emphasised the importance of gunfitting, it is obvious that in a time when money is not what it used to be, many men will perforce be using guns which they have inherited from another generation. While it is not ideal to fit yourself to another person's gun, however good it may be, it is not impossible. The gunfitters and the gun coaches, much the same breed, fit themselves to other people's as part of their day's work. Just by looking along the stocks and barrels they can gauge the angle, by throwing off one way or another to get on target. Some of them can kill clays in test shooting with no better stock than a roughly timbered lump of wood before it is carved into a butt. It is possible to match yourself to a gun in artificial conditions. I wish I could say that it is equally possible to match yourself against driven game in the field.

The gunmakers, at a price, can modify your weapon or weapons. The individual must make up his mind whether it is worth it. There are various ways without plunging into heavy expense, to determine whether your gun suits you. Just suppose that you were some-where in the world where you had to find out for yourself.

I have indicated how you can see shot in the air. I have mentioned that gun coaches can modify the grip and angle in which they hold strange guns to bring them into line with the target. If you are on your own there is no better way of judging how you pattern a particu-lar gun than by firing, at the standard distance of 40yd, at copies of the large format news-papers. Put the target, text up, because you want to know how the pattern shapes top and bottom. It will show you, just as you learn at the shooting school, whether your aim is true. If you have got newspapers you can do without whitewashed plates.

In country practice sessions it is also useful to have somebody standing in a safe decline, fling some of the local fruit over your head. It will do a lot of good to your gunswing.

Always remember that the standard distance at which the two barrels of a shotgun marry is 40yd. If you put up a good performance at that length at a standing target you should not be out of balance, with good gun-mounting, at moving targets. The degree of error, at shorter ranges, is generous.

I have resisted the temptation to attempt an explanation of the complicated craftsmanship which finally arrives at a Best gun. I am not sure that I could make it even interesting. Those who have tried have made it difficult to understand what they are talking about. What they describe may be all very well for a gunmaker's apprentice. For the sportsman, much of the mystery of it is irrelevant.

For a specialist, the evolution of gun actions, so many of them clumsy in the earlier years, is fascinating. It is enough for the sportsman to appreciate that the fashioning of the actions, the barrels and the stock of a Best gun is as subtle as the action of any artifact made today.

If he is building a gun for you the maker will probably invite you to shoot it in his grounds 'in the white'. That means that he wants to try you, and try the gun, before the engraving is done on the furniture and before the metal is blued and hardened. The try-gun, valuable as it it, is heavy, and cannot handle as sweetly as the almost finished arm. A shoot 'in the white' will enable him not only to watch you but to make any minor modifications that the gun needs. It is worth it.

Unless you lack confidence, which means that your gun-mounting is uncertain, do not adopt rubber pads on the butt of your gun, or umbrella rings on your trigger guards to prevent bruised finger. If you learn the drill you will not need them, and the gun will look better without them.

If you are buying a new gun it is possibly advisable to have too much choke in the barrels rather than too little to begin with. Remember that if you take metal out of the barrels you cannot put it back. If you are pernickety, start with too much choke rather than too little.

But at the end of the day, if you employ a top gunmaker, trust him. He will be delighted to sell you all manner of accessories and make any modifications that you ask for. He will think more of you, and help you more, if you just concentrate on shooting straight.

'*Gunpowder was invented in the year 1330 by Swartz of Cologne, and first made in England* AD *1418* (two guesses). *From the number slain in engagements previous to its introduction, what at first view of its fatal effects might be deemed an additional and severe scourge, has rather proved beneficial to Mankind, by reducing destruction of the species in battle, within narrower limits. In providing Man with increased power over the Animal world, and multiplying the catalogue of his food, its advantages are eminent; and, at the present day, Gunpowder is so essential to the Sportsman's success, that its goodness should be his chief concern in his Shooting equipment.*'

DANIEL'S RURAL SPORTS (1807)

'*There is no one point in which the opinions of sportsmen are found to be more diametrically opposed to each other than in the size of shot to be used for shooting game*'.

CAPTAIN LACY (1842)

'*When after the partridges*
You use Eley cartridges'.

PUNCH (1848)

CHAPTER 9

POWDER AND SHOT

If I were writing in the nineteenth century this would be one of the most extensive chapters in the story of the shotgun. It always was in books on shooting in the past. At the end of the twentieth century it is one of the least.

An old gunmaker, on the edge between past and present, argued that you must not blame your cartridges if you miss. He insisted that you must not become a size-of-shot fanatic either. But with memories of loosely loaded cartridges in his youth when powder squibbed and shot charges cartwheeled to leave a large gap in the pattern, or balled into a solid slug, he was defensive. Out of old prejudice he believed that cartridges which were hand-loaded to the customers' requirements, were superior to the factory-manufactured sort.

He harked back to an age, in the days of the muzzleloader and the early breechloaders, when the argument about shot sizes and loads of different powders was clamorous. Experts like General Hangar recommended, unbelievably, 2oz of No2 shot over little more than a dram of powder for all forms of inland shooting. It was comparable to suggesting marbles exploded by a cracker. At the same time there were other shooting men who preferred to put in a couple of drams of powder with about ¾oz of No6 shot. In early days there was some reason for the variation of opinion, because the shot was soft as putty and powder was unpredictable. In our own time cartridges are so standardised, and patterns so regular, that the advice not to blame anybody but yourself if you miss is sound.

As late as the twenties keen shooting men still regarded shot sizes as a matter of importance, even as a cause for secrecy. It is told of a renowned shot that he used to insist that his

Witton ammunition works, near Birmingham

Powder and Shot
Berthold Schwartz, a monk of Freiburg in Germany, discovers the properties of gunpowder (circa 1320)

The dream of an 18th century plumber

In 1782 (Patent No 1347) William Watts, a Bristol plumber, discovered how to make drop shot. It is said that the notion of spilling molten lead into water through a sieve from a height so that it formed like a raindrop came to him in a dream. Before then shot was cut out of strips into dice and rattled into rough spheres. Nobody has improved on his invention of the Shot Tower. The one at Angel Road, Edmonton—like a shotgun barrel—is the factory which still produces most of the shot fired at game in this country. The process, in the words of the technicians, consists in running 'a molten antimony/ lead alloy through a perforated plate'. The refinements of production, which have subsequently developed, are only of interest to another technician. But, basically, nobody has had a better notion than the Bristol plumber's dream. Shot still assumes its spherical shape by being dropped from a tower.

cartridges should be loaded with No4 (a duck shot), but numbered with No6 top wads. Another sportsman swore by 5½ shot and, if circumstances necessitated his using shot of another size, such was his conviction that he never shot so well.

It is true that if you have a taste for various powders for different sizes of shot in different loads for different game at different seasons, it would be unwise to change. You will always shoot best with the cartridges you trust most and, if you think you feel happier with a pink or a brown case, you *will* be happier; and shoot better accordingly.

Until the middle of this century cartridges were still hand-loaded by the gunmakers to

In the early days of the breechloading gun, cartridges were commonly hand-loaded either by the gunmakers or by shooters themselves. Paper cases were made for 4-bores and 8-bores which could be clipped to the length that the wildfowler fancied. Game shots filled their own cartridges with powder and shot to their personal taste. The modern crimped cartridge, marked '6' here, was still to come

Various types of cartridge case

the orders of their customers. It was a matter for discussion whether the powder should be E C or Smokeless Diamond or what-have-you.

The paper and brass cases, embellished with the names of the great makers are now collectors' souvenirs. Multi-coloured, embracing an exotic pattern of varieties from see-through cases to whole brass and deep brass heads, they have littered the grass of the shooting stands of England and the moors of Scotland for generations.

It is perhaps rather a pity that the choice of powder and shot, fun as it was in the past, has less validity now. There are few gunmakers who load their own cartridges, even though their names may appear on the cases. Today a standard crimped cartridge from Eley passes all the tests of pattern and penetration. There are other loaders who have a minority interest, but the great gunmakers have opted out. Cartridges, better in performance than they ever were before, are romantically not quite what they used to be.

The crimp closure, except in larger bores, has largely replaced the rolled turnover. Powder has passed from names to numbers. Size of shot is still the choice of the sportsman. In inland shooting, Nos 5 to 7 are now universal.

The development of the modern cartridge has in fact been rather slower than the evolution of the breechloading gun. The first breakthrough, the first fully integrated cartridge, was a wire cage exploited by the pioneer firm of W. and C. Eley from a French patent in 1827. It had no detonator, but it simplified the process of loading a muzzleloader. It was easier to rod it down a barrel, and it eliminated the use of powder flask and shot pouch. The wire was a de-fouler of the residue left by black powder and, because the container delayed the dispersion of the shot, it added to the effective range of the gun.

It was preceded by the Rev Alexander Forsyth's patent for a detonating gun in 1807, but it was not until 1820–30, after a flush of patents, that most of the conversions from flintlock to percussion were made. The marriage of the wire frame containing powder, wad and shot and the detonating cap was only consummated in the eighteen-sixties. In between there was a short phase of what are known as needle and pinfire arms. The needle and the pin exploded the fulminate inside the cartridge. The first true central fire cartridge in Britain was exhibited by Daw of Threadneedle Street at the Great Exhibition of 1861. There was still a long way to go.

Corrosion of gun metal, induced by the fulminates in the copper caps, was a serious problem. Pretty as they were, the paper cases, even with a deep brass base, swelled in wet weather. The shooter was advised to carry a cartridge extractor in his pocket—as late as the twenties—to root a sticky case out of the breech. When cartridges got wet you had to use a re-sizing ring or bush to reduce them to size. The two problems for the cartridge manufacturers were to produce a weatherproof casing and a non-corrosive cap.

It was not until the late fifties that IMI, the successors of the traditional Eley firm, introduced the first rustless ammunition. It has eliminated most, but not all of the risks of corrosion. Latterly, they introduced the plastic waterproof cartridge case. It ought to have been the final answer; a case, whatever the weather, which never failed to eject, or disappointed in performance.

(*Opposite*) *Pheasants in Flight* by J. C. Harrison

The pageant of the field
The tractor and the Land Rover have taken much of the romance out of a day's shooting. The West Barsham Game Cart, the property of Mr K. D. A. Keith, in Norfolk, preserves a tradition from the past. The artist is Peter Biegel

(*Opposite and page 106*) Victorian equipment used for the home loading of cartridges

It is currently criticised because the plastic cases have been found to be as indestructible as the flint arrow heads of our Stone Age ancestors. Landowners object to the detritus of expended cartridges. Currently, the aim is to produce a cartridge which is weather resistant and which will dissolve into the soil. It is probably very near. In a shooting season in which millions of rounds are ejected the matter is not insignificant.

For the record, no more, the standard 12-bore game cartridge is nominally 2½in long. Pigeon guns take a 2¾in case and wildfowl guns are normally chambered for a 3in case. Though I doubt their effectiveness, special guns chambered for 2in cases, are sometimes favoured. The age of experiment has not quite passed.

The powder and shot controversy has long since been dismissed. That is evident from the sales figures of Eley (IMI) who supply 60 per cent of the current home market. More than three-quarters of all the cartridges fired at game and clay pigeons in a year are now loaded with No5 to No7 shot. No6 represents 40 per cent of the grand total for all forms of shooting.

Cartridge sales, over a sample period of three years, table in this fashion:

10-bore:	0.1%	28-bore:	0.5%
16-bore:	3.2%	410-bore:	6%
20-bore:	3.2%	12-bore:	87%

For a hundred and fifty years, the chore of gun-cleaning after a day's sport was the curse of shooting. It was all very well if you had a reliable servant to do it for you. But you were ill-advised to put a gun away, with the corrosive mischief that could occur, without cleaning the barrels moon-bright.

The non-corrosive cartridge has eliminated most of the risks. With the new cartridges it is notable that you can look up the barrels to find only a fraction of the powder waste you saw in the past. But it is still wise to be careful. The enemy is water. If you have been out in the rain your gun is as much at risk as it was before powder and shot was as clean as it is now. Rust insidiously invades under top ribs and into actions. The prudent shooter, before he puts away his gun, cleans it as carefully as he did before non-corrosive cartridges were invented. It may be added that some imported cartridges had corrosive caps until quite recently, and in many gunrooms and cartridge bags there is an old stock of corrosive ammunition. Have a care. Incidentally, if you have a dirty gun because you have been using obsolete ammunition you can start the cleaning process effectively by firing a couple of rounds of the new clean ammunition through the barrels.

I admit that I myself am not without regret for the past; those shooting seasons in which at the end of the day I cleaned the barrels of my guns, held in a vice in a cushion of leather, until the leading was removed, the metalwork of the actions gleamed, and the walnut stocks glittered with fresh polish. I have a nostalgia for the days of hand-loading. But the shooting man can still enjoy the look of coloured cases ejected on the grass, the patter of spent lead pellets sinking into the coverts, the delicious fragrance of powder smoke hanging in the air on a misty December morning. The fascination of straight powder is timeless.

The Christmas cock-pheasant, he crows on the hill;
His spurs are as javelins, as horn is his bill;
A fox for fine cunning, he's brave to behold,
A Syrian gleaming in purple and gold;
    A sage of fourth season
    He knows the red reason
For stocks in the coverts and 'stops' in the strip,
And back through the beaters he'll modestly slip.

When first season youngsters swing over the trees
To plumb in the open as dead as a cheese
He'll run like a rabbit, he'll squat like a hare
As nothing will make him get up in the air
    The boys hit the hammer
    The tree-trunks and clamour,
The gun on the flank stands in just the right spot,
But he's back up the hedgerow to rise out of shot.

When the last drive's been driven, the last stand been stood,
When the last of the beaters push out of the wood,
When the slowest retriever has ceased to 'seek dead',
Where the snow-powdered stubble rings hard to the tread,
    He's not for the pick-up
    Hark, there's his hard hiccup
Afar in the twilight, blue, jewelled and chill—
The hoary old blackguard who laughs at them still.

PATRICK CHALMERS

CHAPTER 10

FUR AND FEATHER

There is seldom any cause in the field to extend the shotgun beyond its effective performance. Shooting with two double-barrelled guns, or even three as the Victorians sometimes did, is a test of the shooter's ability and agility. The weapons themselves can do it all without trying.

The exception is wildfowling. In shore shooting the eager gunner, with only an occasional chance of a shot, is always tempted to fire at geese and duck which are beyond him. It happens, regrettably, because in the tricky light of a dawn or evening flight on flat salt marshes stretching to the horizon, it is difficult to gauge distance. In inland conditions, with trees to mark height and enclosing hedges to control visibility, it is rare for the quarry to appear out of the shooter's range.

The Americans in particular have engineered repeating and automatic shotguns. They are clumsy weapons which are unwelcome, if sometimes tolerated, in the English shooting field. In fact no man with an automatic arm can compete in speed of practice with one with a pair of side-by-side guns and a loader. The exception is the game of shooting clay targets called skeet. In the field, the tradition in this country is to shoot with precision and above all with restraint.

Without careful ecological control, far from increasing in numbers, there would certainly be less game. It is difficult to teach urban man that this is so; that it is a matter of rule that the fertility of the game crop depends upon selective shooting. Left to itself, nature is a destroyer. The vast crop of game which ornaments Britain is man-made.

If you do not shoot the old stags among deer you will soon have fewer deer. If you do not shoot a partridge manor, partridges will fade away. If you do not cull old cock pheasants, the hens will lay eggs which do not hatch. If grouse are left to themselves and not shot hard in a good year, they will diminish. There are several reasons why. In deer conservation it is essential to kill the old stags to give the fertile youngsters a chance to mate. On partridge ground, the population of birds is increased by breaking up the coveys and ensuring that they do not pair in incestuous relationships. If grouse are left to themselves, with no control over their food resources, they will vacate the moor.

The glory of the shotgun, and indeed the rifle in the Highlands, is that it has provided Britain with the richest game crop in the world. Until the shotgun was developed, game birds, apart from wildfowl, were thin on the ground. Colonel Hawker tells that he had to hunt for a morning, unsuccessfully, for a single cock pheasant in a county which now teems with them. The exploitation of game, however critically it may be viewed by some, provides an important food crop. It has also profited the vastly increased game population which would not have survived at all if man had not multiplied it and looked after its interests in the same way he has looked after his domestic cattle.

In introducing you to the custom of shooting fur and feather I have not attempted a full review of the pattern of its natural history, attractive as the prospect is. There are existing volumes on all the quarry of the field. I have contained my remarks, in the limit of this work, to its relationship with the shotgun. I have put my theme a little out of order in the shooting seasons of the year but, by naming dates, I hope that I have made it easier to understand shotgun practice.

In different climates and in different conditions the close and open seasons for game vary widely, even in Europe. I have named the dates in Britain. I have also ventured to add a few hints on choosing the most succulent game for the table. The hunter is entitled to a good dinner.

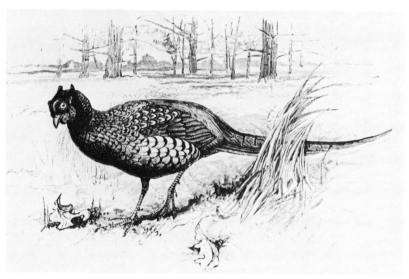

Pheasant

Spring Snow—The Christmas Cock Pheasant by J. C. Harrison

Pheasant

(October 1 to February 1)

It is confidently asserted that the pheasant was introduced into England by the old Romans. I doubt it. In the then savage land that the legionaries invaded, infested with two-legged and four-legged predators, the oriental potentate of the fields would not have stood much of a chance. Armed with slings and arrows it is scarcely likely that even a proconsul could have brought him to table. My own guess is that pheasants in sizeable numbers were first brought to these misty islands by the good missionaries who carried Christianity into the country as well. Surely it was about the abbeys and the monasteries, their lands so studiously cultivated, that the pheasant was domesticated. In medieval documents there is no reference to the pheasant until the middle of the eleventh century. At what time it arrived on these shores remains a mystery. But it is now as much a decoration as ash and oak, the green grass and the golden stubble, the silver streams, and the bronze of falling leaves. He is an immigrant who has truly integrated himself into our own country scene.

The native origin of the species which is still called the Old English Blackneck (*Phasianus colchicus*) was on the River Rion, then called the River Phasis, in the district of Colchis near the Black Sea. The word 'pheasant' derives from the ancient name. It is possible that for hundreds of years no other species of pheasant existed in these islands. It is something of a guess that, with the development of the sea trade with China during the first half of the eighteenth century the Ringnecked pheasant (*P. torquatus*) was introduced.

A third sub-species, the Japanese or Versicolour pheasant arrived in 1840, when a pair were a gift from the King of Italy to the Earl of Derby. The cross-bred Versicolours did not breed true and, at the end of a relatively short period of years, the strain bred out and the Ringneck type dominated. A later strain was the Mongolian (*Phasianus c. mongolicus*), a potent breed imported in the first years of the nineteenth century. The four basic strains have latterly been extended by the development of another sub-species, a dark green-tinted bird now known as a melanistic mutant (*Phasianus* mut. *tenebrosus*).

It is relevant to add that other sub-species may occasionally be encountered in the shooting field. One is the splendid Reeves' pheasant. The cock has tail feathers so long that the bird has a total length of about 6ft. Another is the beautiful golden pheasant, which is properly an aviary bird. Gamekeepers do not like them because they are as quarrelsome as gamecocks. In the breeding season they drive good husbands away from the hens. An occasional sport is an albino. When there is a white pheasant in the coverts you are ill-advised to shoot it. The keeper regards them as pets. He will often report, before a drive begins, that they are sacrosanct.

No pheasant that comes to the gun is pure-bred. The sub-species intermarry regardless. But it is remarkable, when you look at the bag at the end of the day, that four predominant types are still easily identifiable. Our ordinary English pheasants are Colchicus, Torquatus, and Mongolicus, latterly Tenobrosus. Major Hugh B. C. Pollard, of whom I shall have more to say later, has defined the visual difference between them exactly:

'A wealth of personal experience is necessary before you can even guess at a pheasant hen's parentage, but the distinctive features of the pure cocks are fairly easily determined. Colchicus has a purple-black shading to green with *no white neck rings at all*. Torquatus has a white ring which should go *all round*. Mongolicus has the white ring *broken* at the front collar stud when the gold chestnut of the upper breast pins the iridescent neck, and is much broader, and Versicolour (it is now much rarer) is a metallic green, not gold-bronze, with no neck ring at all. The mutant has no indented Japanese flank feathers. Seen pure it is easy, but when we come to look at the serried rows which mark the last stand, identification, as they say in the police reports, is not so simple. The ring basis no longer holds good, for the blood is mixed.

The eye and the rump are perhaps the next best points. Colchicus has a yellow brown eye in keeping with his neat uniform, and a dark maroon rump, Torquatus has a white eyebrow and a grey-blue, almost lavender-coloured rump, and the same kind of colour on the wings, where those of Colchicus are bronze-brown. Mongolicus has a very light pale yellow eye, white patched wings, and is a larger bird than the others. Versicolour colour crosses are still dark metallic in the overlay of ordinary feathering, and the flank feathers bear an identical bar like a Japanese war fan in place of the straight bar or lancet of the others. No mutant cross is known; they appear to breed clean, normal or mutant. The very light hens are usually Mongolians or first cross Mongolians, and have very light yellow eyes. Very dark hens are either Versicolour or mutant. In the case of the latter the rump is usually green-plumaged. In the past, very light bleached-looking birds, either cocks or hens, were often called Bohemian pheasants. They are, in fact, albinistic mutants and not a true sub-species, but sports . . .'

Major Pollard probes deeper than I fancy the average shooter will wish to go. But it is wise, and satisfying, to know your quarry. It is not quite enough to have a good gun under your arm.

The pattern of the shooting season for pheasants in Britain is now well established. The custom on every shoot is that in October, when the season begins, only the outside boundaries of an estate are shot. The object is to push the stragglers into the home coverts where the birds were reared and are still regularly fed. The big shoots are always in November when the leaf is off the trees. In the latter months, the order of the day varies in accordance with the stock on the ground. At the back-end as it is called, 'cocks-only' is the normal shooting practice. It is sometimes reversed. Cocks are shot at the start of the season. Hens are a permissible target only when the keepers have penned a sufficient stock to provide enough eggs, about thirty a bird, for the next year.

It is sometimes argued that pheasant shooting is an artificial sport. The case has a certain validity. Unlike any other game, the pheasant responds to human control. It can be contained in a limited area and, with skilled management, presented on the wing to a line of guns in the field. If it were possible, for example, to organise wood pigeons in the same way, I often wonder whether they would not be regarded as better sport.

At its worst, pheasant shooting is open to criticism. At its best the man who makes it is the gamekeeper. In the discipline of a good shoot nobody raises his gun to a low bird or a close one. The art of driving pheasants, the art of placing the stands, is to show the birds as tall and fast as they can fly. The best stands are counted those between coverts where the undulation of the ground offers the most challenging shot; those places which, as an experienced gun once suggested to me, you shoot before you see them.

Make no mistake. Pheasant shooting at its best is not easy. It is estimated that a pheasant in full flight moves at 38–40mph. With the wind in his tail he curves unpredictably. You have to be a good shot to put up a creditable performance.

The custom on big shoots is to give every gun a gift of a pair, even two pairs, of grace birds. The recipient seldom has an opportunity of making a choice. But it is well to know what it is that distinguishes a bird for the table.

A November pheasant, fat on blackberries, acorns and beechmast, stuffed with corn from the stubble, is undoubtedly the best table bird of all. The spur on his legs, unless they are aggressively sharp, are not a sure guide to his birthday. Normally, he will be a bird of the year. Late pheasants, shot in December and January, are good enough, but they are never quite the same as birds culled in the season when you can pick eating chestnuts off the ground to stuff them. Old birds will improve with hanging. I have heard it said that a January cock pheasant need not be served until Easter, whatever the date appointed by the Pope.

Partridge
(September 1 to February 1)
The autumnal-coloured grey partridge, so unassuming in his appearance, is to most sportsmen the most beloved of all game birds. Unlike the pheasant he is a native of our own green pastures, the stubbled corn lands, the secret places in the underworld of root crops and hedgerows, the feathered brother of the windswept leaves. In the language of sport the partridge alone is designated as 'a bird' with the same respect that, in angling, a salmon is

Grey or English partridge

always 'a fish'. Other species, lesser creatures within the law, are known by their generic names. Like kings and queens, it is recognised that partridges and salmon are creatures apart from the common breed.

Arguably, partridge shooting is the best shooting of all. Unequivocally, there is no dish on earth to compare with a fat young partridge, lovingly roasted, as an epicurean delight. A wit has remarked that, 'A perfectly cooked partridge, the accompanying perfect bottle, and a delightful but tentatively imperfect companion, offers a temptation that few can deny or regret.'

For the shooter it is important to add that partridges often seem possessed by the devil. They do not fly at the speed of pheasants and grouse, or wild duck. In full flight they average about 32–36mph. But their habit is wildly disconcerting to any but the coolest shot. When a covey is flushed during a drive it is customary for the keepers to sound a whistle. Often enough the whistle is sufficient to make a man tense on his gun and, when the flurry of birds comes over, miss yards behind. An average covey of partridges is likely to number about seven to fifteen. In the excitement when they top the hedgerows the shooter is always liable to 'blind into the brown' instead of fixing his eyes on a single bird. Because he hasn't selected his bird, the chances are that his shot charge will be placed in the gaps between birds rather than at any single one of them. If you panic when you sight a covey of partridges—and how easy it is to do so—you will assuredly miss.

It is noticeable that, if a single bird breaks over the guns, he is almost certainly killed. There is no distraction to the eye. When that happens you may reasonably assume that he is a

(*Opposite*) *Portrait of the Partridge*—(Frenchman) a watercolour by Rodger McPhail

Grey Partridge Rising—a watercolour by J. C. Harrison

'Frenchman'. Unlike the grey or English partridge, he is a stranger introduced into this country during the seventeenth and eighteenth centuries. It is even questionable whether he is a true partridge in our definition of the species at all. The hen lays a mottled egg quite unlike the olive-green of our own birds and although ornithologists have sometimes claimed that the English partridge mates with them there is no evidence to support the theory. The coloration of the bird, which is very pretty, relates more closely to the Chukar of Near Asia and the Indian hills. There is no question that the Frenchmen have settled happily in most partridge manors although nobody has yet finally determined how to describe them. They are variously described as French or Guernsey partridges, Hungarian partridges, or just 'red-legs'. It is interesting that they are the most common partridges in the meseta of Spain, where the shooting is quite exceptionally good.

In our great-grandparents' time, when partridges were walked up rather than driven, 'the red-legs' were unpopular. The reason is that they prefer to run before they fly. Today, in driven shooting, the Frenchmen are often the first birds over the guns. As they often fly in isolation they give the gun a chance to settle in before the coveys of Englishmen put him on his mettle. It is worth adding that most cooks agree that for the table, the Frenchmen do not compare with the English birds. Although handsome and a little heavier, they are, I feel, rather coarser.

Although the legal season for partridges extends as long as the season for pheasants very few estates, or sportsmen, take full advantage of it. The partridge, unlike the pheasant, does not respond easily to domesticity. Even now, when great advances have been made in breeding partridges in artificial conditions, it is by no means certain that it increases stock on the ground. At best it costs a lot of money to put down birds on a manor. It is a tricky art to spread pairs over a breeding territory. It is useless, after raising birds in pens, to turn them out in packs when they will be unmanageable.

On the whole the partridge, like the cat who walked by himself, still insists on being alone. It is unhappily true that he flourishes best on the worst-farmed lands. What he likes is untidy cover, ant-heaps and tons of weed seeds. The fact that the partridge crop has been uneven for many years may be ascribed directly to better husbandry. In the best-farmed country in the world the partridge is a loser.

It is customary now, on most properly run estates, to shoot partridges with reservation. Irrespective of the legal limits they are not shot after December. In early September it is useful to break up the coveys, scatter the young birds (they are a monogamous species), to mate with strangers. By December they are on an iron ration of frozen greenstuff. As table birds at that time of year, they are undistinguished. In January they pack in preparation for the bridal season in the spring. There is a saying that, if it is fine for Royal Ascot in June, when most of the chicks hatch, it will be a good partridge year. We should look after them. They are the best that we have got.

Woodcock (September 1 to February 1)

In the list of our game birds the woodcock scarcely commands a place except under the category 'various'. Yet, in the mystique of shotgun shooting, a woodcock is literally a feather in the cap of any gun who bags him.

They are strange creatures. Most of them are immigrants although a few regularly breed in this country. I once found a nest of four eggs, and I swear that I have seen one carrying its chicks between its legs roding in West Sussex. They are night birds, with beautiful boot-button eyes, who seem to lose vision in broad daylight. With their long beaks they live on worms, and probably a variety of other mud-dwelling insects. Like the nightjar they are the subject of superstition. The immigrants arrive, tens of thousands of them, in the November moon. Homing largely in East Anglia, they spread over the country.

Our forefathers valued them for the table. A woodcock on toast, its entrails dripping into the butter, was counted a treat. I have never shared their taste for the black meat any more than I enjoy that other worm-eater, the snipe. I fancy that our palates have changed. But there is no doubt that the woodcock, more than any other bird, enjoys the reputation of being the prime target of the shooting field.

Quite reasonable shots in a pheasant drive seem to lose their heads when the beaters shout 'cock-up' It is the most tired joke in the shooting field that a veteran gamekeeper attributed his long life to the fact that he always threw himself flat on his face whenever he heard the call of 'cock' in the coverts. Woodcock are not difficult shooting. Their fascination with their silent flight is that they are unexpected strangers.

Woodcock

Leaving the coverts—Woodcock, a watercolour by J. C. Harrison

The magic of woodcock lies partly in the past. In early times the two pin- or pen-feathers out of his wing were valued by miniaturists as brushes, and were probably used in illuminating medieval manuscripts by the monks. You will find them behind the primary feathers. If you turn the bird upside-down, stretch out his wings, and look one-third of the way down from the top angle, you will discover the sharp-pointed pinions which were so valued by men who created great art. These days you will usually notice them in the bands of game-keepers' hats.

Tradition also requires that, when a woodcock is shot, he is legged. The sinews are drawn out of his thighs so that he is tenderer for the table. I am sorry that I cannot recommend them in my day as enthusiastically as young partridges. But others may say that I am wrong.

The magic that this bird has for sportsmen was expressed by Sir Jowell Buston MP in his journal as follows: 'Talk to me of the excitement of the House of Commons—the best debate will not beat good woodcock-shooting.'

Grouse
(August 12 to December 10)

Driven grouse, in a good year and at their glorious best, offer the most exhilarating challenge to a shotgunner of any game bird in any country in the world. It is partly because the shooter is reduced to size in the wild grandeur of the scenery in the purple hills; partly because there is nowhere else, outside the British Isles, and then only in certain parts of it, where the soil is predominantly acid with an adequate growth of the right type of bell heather and a sufficiency of quartz grit on which *Lagopus scoticus* flourishes. But there are other reasons.

There are related birds in other lands called grouse but the indigenous species, the muir

Red Grouse

A Grouse Drive—a watercolour by J. C. Harrison

fowl of Scotland, is unique. As a table bird, cold roast grouse and a porridge of Scottish oats is the ultimately perfect breakfast. The bird ranks in the epicurean calendar with the partridge and the pheasant. In their respective seasons no discerning cook would care to place the importance of one before the other two. But, above all, the real grouse presents what is incomparably the greatest test in the art of shooting.

Cautiously, I have qualified that eulogy with the reservation 'in a good season and at their best'. There is no law of the Medes and the Persians that grouse-shooting will always provide the excellent sport expected of it. In the coverts after pheasants, and in the partridge manors, you may be reasonably certain of the bag. On the moors it is anyone's guess on the Glorious Twelfth of August, the opening day of the season, what stock there will be to sweep over the butts.

There is a certain mystery in the matter. In the bare hills even a Highland keeper, with legs as hard as bog oak, can scarcely walk more than a fraction of his land. He cannot and will not give a promise how many birds he has in the heather. The grouse, in strange migratory movements, will overnight leave one moor for another for reasons which are still beyond explanation. J. K. Stanford wrote a splendid story called *The Twelfth* in which he told how, after a stroke, the spirit of a calloused old shooting colonel was translated into the body of a grouse. He organised the birds in military fashion so that, on the big day, they migrated to safer territory. Occasionally, it is easy to suppose that someone like that tips the birds the wink to fly wild on what should have been good drives.

Another hazard is that there is reason to suppose that the grouse population rises and falls in cycles. The period is believed to be about seven years. After a peak year, perhaps because the food crop is inadequate or stocks are thinned by disease (usually parasitic worms), the birds disappear. It can also come about after a season in which the moor has been rented by rich but ineffective shots. If the grouse are not shot hard in one season they will fail in the next one. It is the same ecological rule which applies to keeping up a healthy partridge stock. Parasitic diseases flourish as they do in human communities when there is over-population and inclement weather.

Renting a grouse moor in Scotland and the northern English counties now costs a fortune and it is therefore always a gamble to assume that a four thousand bird moor one year will prove as fertile in the next year. Looking at the record over the years, it appears that a northern English moor is likely to prove more consistent than one in the Highlands of Scotland.

The far north remains a country, the loveliest of all, in which the old way of shooting over pointers and setters is still predominant. Dogging grouse, enchanting as the sport is, does not make the same challenge of skill that driven birds demand. Generally it is not difficult to make good practice. But as a test for the young and fiercely energetic, lifting their legs through the thick heather after the ranging dogs, the traditional sport is not to be discounted. It is not work for somebody who is other than in top condition.

Even the comparative comfort of waiting in the butts on an organised grouse drive is a test of physique. You normally have to march up a hill a quarter of a mile or so to get into position. The vast landscape looks so empty that a shooter may wonder if there is any game in the heather at all. The beaters are likely to be a mile away. The stones or earth in the butt squelch underfoot in the peat bogs. You appear to be nowhere in nowhere.

The butts are arranged in a half-circle because the grouse fly on the lines of the contours in the hills. In a well-organised shoot, the keepers put sticks on either side of the butt as a warning to the gun not to swing beyond them on either side. Grouse-shooting, because of the arrangement of the butts, is particularly liable to shooting accidents. In your own butt you will wait a long time, stamping your feet, before anything happens.

You need to keep particularly calm. If you have a loader, or a companion, you must instruct him to keep well down, and quite still. You all ought to be wearing caps and heather-coloured tweeds. Camouflage is unnecessary in pheasant shooting, because pheasants choose their flight line, and usually stick to it, but you would be unwise not to cover your forehead with a cap when you are partridge-shooting. In the case of grouse you would be mad not to sink yourself into the landscape if you hope to have a good chance against driven grouse. At the sight of you they will all jink down the line.

If you are unfamiliar with grouse-shooting you will almost certainly make a botch of the first covey or the first singleton, which bursts into your vision. With the wind in their tails, and they do not give you warning that that are coming, they are probably travelling anything between 30—50mph. Hanging on to the contour of the ground they are often not more than 4ft above the heather. Their eyes, stuck well out in front, will hypnotise you into holding your trigger. They will be over and gone before you know what has happened.

Whatever you do don't blast off as they go over the hill, or more often down the hill, behind you.

The place to kill grouse is well-in-front. What is wanted is a lift of the gun, and fire, at the moment that you sight them. An old mentor of mine used to say that you press the trigger 'at the moment that they look big enough to eat'. It suited him. My own rule is to shoot on first sight. I may not be good at it. But it is far better than hanging about for second sight.

Capers

Capers and Black Game
(August 20 to December 10)
The largest of Britain's game birds is the wood grouse or capercailzie (also spelt caper-caillie). The word is a corruption of the Gaelic 'Great Cock of the Woods' although it is unlikely that the Gaels even tried to spell it. Sportsmen, with good reason, generally refer to the bird as a 'caper' (pronounced 'capper').

The average weight of a mature cock is anything between 9 and 12lb and of a hen 4—7lb, although birds much heavier have been recorded in Scandinavia and Russia. By comparison a red grouse averages about 1-lb, a big cock pheasant 3—4lb.

Black game

Tetrao urogallus, essentially a bird of the woodlands, was indigenous until it became extinct, possibly through loss of forest lands, in the late eighteenth century. It was reintroduced from Scandinavia by the Marquis of Breadalbane in Perthshire in the early nineteenth century. Thanks largely to the activities of the Forestry Commission in this century the spruce plantations have provided an ideal habitat for the bird which flourishes on the tender shoots of the trees.

As a game bird the caper enjoys the same sort of reputation as the woodcock. He is a surprise target. He is often missed because, on account of his great size. he appears to be flying slower than his wing beat suggests. In fact he can turn a better show of speed than a red grouse. I have killed capers, with the wind in their tails, when they have burst their crops when they hit the ground. As table birds, I cannot recommend them. When shooting parties arrive from the North at King's Cross Station in London, with their hampers of game, you can smell the turpentine of capers all down the platform. I do not serve them in my own dining-room. But they are an exciting addition to the bag. Hugh Gladstone, in his book *Record Bags and Shooting Records*, notes that in Scotland at the beginning of this century nearly a hundred were killed on several occasions in a single day's shooting. But that is not the general rule; nor is it desirable for a bird which is culinarily unappetising. It is incidental that, during the nineteenth century, attempts were made to introduce the American wild turkey, a bird of similar size to the caper, to Britain. It is no great loss that the experiment failed. We are better with the splendid game birds we have already got.

It is unusual to find what are called black game on the same ground as capers and red grouse. Black game are lovely romantic birds which make their homes where the moors and foothills break down into a girdle of birch woods and sparse coverts adjoining agricultural ground. The blackcock is the bird—his mate is called a greyhen—which provides the lyre-shaped tails which ornament the glengarries of the Highland pipers, and the Highland regiments.

The ptarmigan (*Lagopus mutus cinereus*) is a bird of the mountain tops. He is seldom found below the 2,500ft level. Because of the places where he lives he is rarely shot. He is not collected for the table; more often he is stuffed and displayed in glass cases to exhibit his snow-white winter plumage.

Snipe
(August 1 to March 1)
In the shooting season in Britain, snipe are occasional birds, although there are few patches of marshland in which they are not in occupation. It is only in Ireland that any attempt is made to drive them over guns. Normally, they are walked up over dogs. Nevertheless,

Snipe

(*Opposite*) *Snipe in Winter's Grip*—a watercolour by J. C. Harrison

J.C.Harrison.

because they enjoy a reputation as a test of shotgun practice, I have included them here.

We have two species, the common snipe (*Gallinago coelestis*) and the little Jack-snipe (*Gallinago gallunula*). There is a third, the Great Snipe, which is an irregular visitor and which I have never seen in my life. In the past century snipe were valued on toast as a breakfast dish. I scarcely know anyone who has ever eaten one. Served with their entrails inside them, like a woodcock, they are at best a titbit. But their reputation as birds of the chase persists.

To one who is inexperienced in the sport it is true that the tricky flight of the bird is exasperating. But Colonel Hawker, using a flintgun, claimed that he shot fifteen in a row. Truthfully it is trick shooting. When a wisp of snipe blows off a marsh in the wind you must, above all, be quick. You should shoot at the moment when the bird turns in the air after the initial spring from the ground to show you the white of its rump. It is the same moment that the snipe drops a spot of lime as it throws-over to settle into its characteristic zig-zag flight. If you wait until the bird settles on its course you will be just plumb lucky if you make a kill. To be certain, you must catch it when it hangs momentarily in the air between the lift from the ground and the going-away flight.

Experienced snipe shots count it so important to kill their bird at the psychological moment that many of them will shoot before their gun is properly settled into their shoulder. You will make incalculable misses at snipe if you shoot with shot larger than No8. They can fly between the gaps in the pattern.

Wood Pigeons
(No close season)

In a lifetime, Colonel Peter Hawker, according to his own carefully kept records, shot only 20 wood pigeons and 318 rabbits. Living in the county of Hampshire, which was infested with both, it is only possible to suppose that, with a flintgun, he could only shoot them sitting. A contemporary pigeon shot expects to kill a hundred in a day.

In this country where all shooting, except wildfowling on the foreshore, is closely controlled, wood pigeons are anybody's quarry. With the permission of an amiable farmer, satisfied that you will not shoot his game birds, you are welcome to as many as you can kill. Wood pigeons are a pest. It happens that they also provide some of the best shotgun shooting of all.

Pigeons are shot over decoys at harvest or, best of all, in February in mass shoots when all the surrounding coverts are manned to catch them when they come in to roost. It is said that anyone who can kill one out of four flighting wood pigeons is a good shot. I might add that anyone who can put up a twenty-five per cent performance to cartridges expended at any bird that flies is a first class shot, whatever claims are made to the contrary.

Wood pigeons are a challenge because their abundant blue feathers make them seem much larger than they are. They will drop feathers even when you have missed. In reasonable light it is a good rule to shoot only when you see the white collar round their necks, or the orange of their eyes.

Hares and Rabbits
(No close season)

In the exercise of shotgun skills the shooting of fur is not rated highly. In partridge and

Hare

pheasant shoots hares and rabbits are usually listed among 'various'. Most men who shoot dislike killing hares, although a great many enjoy tumbling a rabbit. Both are, agriculturally, pests.

Before the unpleasant disease myxomatosis virtually wiped out the wild rabbit throughout Europe, Britain swarmed with them. The Victorian landowners, who cultivated warrens, killed thousands in a day's shooting. Until the early fifties, when the disease struck, it was difficult to drive a car at night without knocking over a few on the way. Myxomatosis, which the rabbits pick up from a flea in their burrows, and which appears to be endemic, has virtually destroyed what in the past was the commonest creature in the British country-side. Rabbits appear in pockets, only to be knocked out again by the fatal disease.

In farming terms, it is a blessing. The reduction of the rabbit population has probably added the equivalent output of two counties to the grain production of this country. But it is probably that for the sportsman, rich and poor, the demise of the rabbit is a loss. He provided more fun, and food, than any other animal in the fields and woods. Hunting him with ferrets and snares, shooting him in the harvest field, was a national sport. Without him, Britain is not quite the same.

It is interesting that a rhyme on rabbit shooting, which can scarcely be faulted, was written by a certain Mr Watts in the early years of the nineteenth century:

'More difficult than hares to hit,
They frequently appear to flit
Like shadows past; good indeed,
Is then the aim that makes them bleed.
If you would see them nicely stopped
In the thick wood, you must adopt
Snap-shooting, for you'll seldom there
Have time to take them full and fair;
E'en lost to view, advance your gun
Quickly to where you think they run;
Regard not grass, nor bush, nor briar,
Through each and all that instant fire.
Bang! it is well—you saw him not,
And yet you've killed him on the spot.'

In the days before the disease struck it was always the rabbits, not the hares, that the beaters wanted to take home as a gift from the shooting party. In a hungrier age, hares were highly valued for the table. In a broiler chicken age the palate for rich meat has diminished. The buyers, after great hare drives in February in the Home Counties, are almost all from the middle European countries. We ourselves have largely lost our taste for jugged hare.

The shotgunner has largely lost his taste, if he ever had it, for shooting them. Hares, apart from deer which are no longer regarded as beasts of the chase outside Scotland, are the largest quarry shot in Britain. The average full grown weight is 8—9lb, but I have killed one in Hampshire of 13lb. They are not a test of shooting skill.

They are a trouble in the field where, because of their size, shooters suppose that they are closer to the range of the gun than in fact they are. They cry pathetically when they are wounded.

It is nevertheless necessary that the population of hares be kept under rigid control. I know estates in the chalklands where fourteen thousand have to be killed in a fortnight in the late winter. But it is a pity.

When hares lollop up to you in a drive it is easy, if you know the form, to hold your gun to lift the ground under their feet. When they offer a crossing shot at full gallop they are at their most vulnerable. They are dangerous to other guns when they appear in a drive. The swing down the line has caused more accidents in the field than any other.

I recollect an incident when a famous gunmaker was loading for royalty. He warned His Royal Highness not to shoot in front as a hare broke covert. A moment or two later two distracted lovers broke covert at the point where His Royal Highness was about to shoot.

The lesson, in the exercise of the shotgun, is never to shoot fur in front as it is a rule that a good gun always shoots well ahead at flying game. A hare should always be taken behind. Rabbits, bouncing through the rides, provided excellent sport for the quick shot. Hares have never been more than game for a steadily diminishing demand for the table.

I shall be happy if I never shoot a hare again. While it is necessary in their season to destroy them, there is no pleasure in the job. The charm of shotgun shooting is the difficulties of it. The best of it is wondering why you miss.

Wildfowl

Shotgun shooting, as we understand it, was not part of the world of Colonel Peter Hawker in the nineteenth century. His notion was to arm himself with the largest cannon he could devise to devastate the wildfowl population of Lymington in Hampshire, where he had a cottage. He bravely ventured out with his punt guns in unwelcoming winter weather. He called a handgun, in his adventures on the saltings, a cripple-stopper.

Punt-gunning is now the sport of the very few. Wildfowling is the pursuit of an ever increasingly number of sportsmen. It is possible that more cartridges are expended by wildfowlers now than were expended in the heyday of rich man's Edwardian shooting.

Colonel Hawker, and his like, used bigger and bigger guns to reduce rafts of wildfowl on the saltings. Subsequently, it became fashionable to adopt fowling guns of huge bore. 8- and 10-bore pieces, even with black powder, had a kick like a mule. The shotgun flourished on size.

Contemporarily, the best gun for shotgun work is a full-choked 12-bore weapon chambered for 3in cartridges. It is best if it is a plain gun, a boxlock for preference. Sidelocks, which essentially cost more, are unsuited to the hard conditions of wildfowling. Any gun used for wildfowling must be treated with libations of linseed oil. Salt plays merry hell with lock, stock and barrel.

Various

With few exceptions, all birds other than gamebirds are protected in Britain. The gun may only be used, lawfully to eliminate predators like the crow family, who were actually listed as pests in the time of Henry VIII; and in unusual circumstances and with special permission birds like bullfinches which prey on fruit crops.

The law is almost universally accepted. Small boys do not collect songbirds' eggs any more. People do not shoot when they see something on the wing which appears strange.

But the custom in the field is still to kill jays or magpies, those which are foolish enough to fly over the guns. They are enemies of their own kind, feeding on the eggs of more desirable species.

There is also an art to it. A jay with its lilting flight, can be a difficult target. A feather from his blue-spangled wing is a decoration to any shooting cap. It matches with a pin-feather from a woodcock.

Game Birds of the Past

Britain, so rich in game birds, has lost several species which figured largely in the old books of the chase, including the biggest of the native species and one of the smallest.

It is said that the last Great Bustard (*O. tarda*) of the British race was killed in Norfolk in 1838. The great bird, the males are supposed to have grown to a weight of 36lb, once flourished on the chalklands of Salisbury Plain and the heaths and brecks of East Anglia. With its great weight and heavy flight, it was hunted to extinction, largely by army officers

Great Bustard

on horseback at the turn of the nineteenth century. Attempts are still being made to reintroduce it. But it is questionable whether the Great Bustard has any place, outside parklands and zoos, in the modern agricultural scene. It may be regarded as a bird which was overtaken by modern times.

It is sadder that our sporting scene has lost the little quail (*Coturnix coturnix*). A miniature partridge, it was once counted one of the greatest delicacies of the table. Today it is replaced by a domestically-reared bird, overtly introduced from China. Its eggs and flesh are no match for its predecessor.

Corncrake

In my shooting life I have only once seen a bevy of quail, which were in a crop of flax in the South country. I have also seen a few singletons, but I have never raised my gun to them.

They have vanished from the country scene because, on their migration flight, they are netted on the Mediterranean coast of Africa, on the heights of the otherwise sweet Isle of Capri, and in other Latin places.

A third game species, the exquisitely-named corncrake, is now almost extinct. Once common in the cornfields it used to be hunted with decoys which imitated the crake's voice. It brought them to the gun. They flourished in the days of more primitive farming methods. They have perished, sadly, as the machine has taken over. In the wild I have seen one, only one, in my shooting life.

'The Woman said, "Wild Thing out of the Wild Woods, help my man to hunt through the day and guard this Cave at night, and I will give you as many roast bones as you need."

Wild Dog crawled into the Cave and laid his head on his Woman's lap, and said, "Oh my Friend and Wife of my Friend, I will help your man to hunt through the day, and at night I will guard your Cave."

When the Man waked up he said, "What is Wild Dog doing here?" And his Woman said, "His name is not Wild Dog any more, but the First Friend, because he will be our friend for always and always. Take him with you when you go hunting." '

RUDYARD KIPLING
(Just So Stories)

CHAPTER 11

GUNDOGS

The development of the shotgun during the nineteenth century is essentially parallelled in the evolution of the modern breeds of dogs. Among the many consequences following the introduction of the breechloader, and not least the steam train, was a change in the ecology of Britain. A new way of life was created for its more fortunate inhabitants, and even some of the less fortunate. The pattern of centuries was overthrown. Not least, it elevated the dog into civilized society.

Until the eighteenth, and almost into the middle of the nineteenth century, nobody had much interest in dogs. They were the jackals of human society. Packs of hounds were cultivated for the chase. Domestic dogs were judged, not for their charm, but for fierceness and their ability to drive off intruders. 'Cave canem', the brute discovered on the doorstep of a villa in Pompeii, represents the attitude of two thousand years of human history.

Toy dogs were cultivated, like the sleeve dogs of Good King Charles, but nobody thought of them as dogs. They were freaks. Dogs were the curs to which Henry VIII flicked a bone on the straw-covered castle floor. The mastiffs, which Good Queen Bess would have called bandogs, were used to bait bears, bulls and badgers for amusement. Humanity may be regarded as a Victorian invention.

Until Victorian times there was no classification of breeding. Dogs were either fighting dogs, hunting dogs or herd and flock guardians. It seems that they separated into four groups. First there was the greyhound or gaze-hound, who used his eyes and his speed to run down his quarry. There is good evidence, dating back to Assyrian times that his line has survived for two thousand years. The rest is speculation. It is anybody's guess that the other three types, in a species which produces something as ridiculously small as the Yorkshire terrier and so abnormally large as the Great Dane, have the same genes. But it appears that there are three other types which may possibly provide the origins of all the breeds we have defined today: the wolf or shepherd dog (the Alsatian), the water-dog (the poodle and the spaniel), and the mastiff (out of which we get the terriers, and other small breeds).

The table of dogs' genealogical trees is most unsatisfactory. Nobody really knows. I am confident that the index we have today on straight-line breeding was initiated by country gentlemen, shepherds and gamekeepers in the early nineteenth century. In their way, without any knowledge of the finer points of breeding which had not then been established they cultivated a line of working dogs of their own. Without knowing it they were creating breed classifications. The Duke of Newcastle encouraged a heavy type of spaniel, named a Clumber after the name of his country seat, a dog which later enjoyed the favour of King George V. Parson Jack Russell, in the West Country, made his own choice of hunt terriers which survive in his name, with a thumb-print mark on their rump which identifies them to this day.

In Gainsborough's portrait of Thomas Coke (1782) the dogs at his feet are named as Gordon setters bred from a bitch which Coke gave to the Duke of Gordon. To our eyes they are spaniel sort. In Stonehenge's work of 1867 the illustration for the black-and-tan or Gordon setter was that of a dog named 'Kent'. Edward C. Ash, in his *History of Dogs* (1927) writes scathingly that he was 'the most appalling-looking mongrel, with perhaps enough setter about him to let us know what he is supposed to be'. Such were the difficulties of the identification of type as late as the beginning of the twentieth century.

Breeds, now so fashionable, like the English springer, were rescued from gamekeepers' cottages where they had not been recognised at all. In a sort of secrecy, in landowners' houses, in shepherds' crofts, in gamekeepers' cottages, it was suddenly realized that there were generations of working dogs which belonged to a new age. They themselves, although there was no breed classification, were in a true line.

It is an indisputable fact that in towns during the nineteenth century the streets were littered with mongrels, turned out as often as not by unfortunate and needy families. At that time it was difficult to organise a proper ordering of breeds. Even into the twentieth century the pavements were littered with curs of impossible parentage which still fouled the streets.

The classification of dog breeds has all come about in little more than a hundred years. In 1859 the first dog show was promoted by Mr Pape, a local sporting gunmaker, and a Mr Shorthose. The prizes were Mr Pape's own guns. He was a good maker of his time. Twenty-three pointers and twenty-seven setters were entered. On April 18, 1865, the first field trial took place at Southall, near Bedford. In April 1873 the Kennel Club was formed. In 1874, the first KC Stud Book was published.

The Kennel Club is now the commanding influence on everything affecting dogs. It defines the breeds and the standards which may be accepted. Its judges are expert in apprais-ing the points which decide between the champions and the runners-up. It has done more than any organisation in the world to raise the dog in the social calendar, from the cur to the gentleman. But I confess to reservations.

For shooting, the dog's Derby, the search for the champion at Cruft's, is unreal. It is too much like the choice of 'Miss World'. I still prefer a dog who can be judged on performance.

That is why my own heart is in what are called field trial dogs, dogs tested in the field over the guns. They have no expectation of a place in the showring. Their pedigree only counts the record of Field Trial Champions in their line. But it is a precious one.

It is a tradition that Spaniel field trial dogs are only cropped in the last inch of their tails. It is important to do this to a gundog because, when spaniels range in covert, they have a tendency to bloody the tips. If you remove just a little bit, their tails are still long enough to cover their parts, and still keep them out of trouble. The difference between a field trial spaniel and the show bench one is that one has a stump and the other a vibrating stern which talks to you as you carry your gun beside him.

Driven gameshooting has changed tastes in dogs. In muzzleloading days, the working dogs were a pair of pointers or setters. They are still used effectively for walking up grouse in the Highlands but, below the heather line, they have little practical value. Today the stubble is stripped so thin by the combine harvesters that holding cover is negligible. Setters, beautiful as they are ranging out, are too riotous to control easily. Pointers, beautifully honouring their owner's signal with quivering lifted leg, so seldom have the country they need now in southern England.

In our generation the shooting field is the world of the Labrador and the spaniel. The history of the Labrador, black and yellow, is still comparatively short. He was first recognised by the Kennel Club in 1903. It is said that Lord Malmesbury had a kennel from 1837 to 1870, and that Holland Hibbert had a kennel in the eighties. But, like most dog history, the facts are hazy.

Yet there is no doubt that no dog has been cozened in the age of the breechloader more carefully than the 'Lab'. A short-coupled dog, with an otter tail, is the perfect accompaniment to a gun and his loader in the field. In practice it may be argued that the Labrador, so obedient and so generally quiet, is the ideal retriever. Where he sometimes fails is that he funks heavy cover, a situation in which no spaniel ever gives up.

The trouble with spaniels is that it is rare for them to accept total discipline. If they do it usually means that the fire has been beaten out of them. You cannot have it both ways.

One of the hopes of shooting men is to discover the all-purpose gundog. Such a dog is very rare. I think that I have encountered one in my life, a cross between a Labrador and a spaniel; a bitch who, at the wave of a hand, would hunt in front, come to heel on a whistle, and retrieve a runner. She did it, but by and large I believe that it is too much to ask of a dog to serve every need.

But I can never overlook the relationship between a man's gun and his dog. I have had dogs who were gun-shy; but I think of those who pressed their nose prints, to my mild exasperation, on the barrels as they stood in the racks. When I picked up one of the guns they cried with anticipated joy. A shotgun is only half a weapon without a good dog at your side.

(*Opposite*)
The primitive prints of the late eighteenth and nineteenth centuries reveal the sporting world of our forebears. In their top hats, with their clumsy muzzleloaders, they could only afford a raking shot at going-away birds put up by their pointers and setters. Their world is enchantingly human and fallible. In all the prints, their world is depicted as colourful and pleasant. By contrast look at the water colour by the great sporting artist of our time J. C. Harrison. He accurately depicts a driven cock pheasant, curling in the wind, as a bouquet of birds bursts over the guns. The new school of sporting artists records the picture that the shooting man sees

'The stately homes of England, how beautiful they stand,
To prove the upper classes have still the upper hand.'

NOEL COWARD

'Ladies, as a rule, are not "sportsmen", and except perhaps occasionally joining the
shooting party on the hill at lunch, are in many cases doomed to the monotony of the lodge.
It will thus be seen that nice walks, tennis and croquet lawns, and proximity to a golf
course are a great acquisition.'

TOM SPEEDY (1920)

CHAPTER 12

COUNTRY HOUSE PARTIES

The impact of the shotgun on society, unremarked by historians who mostly live far away from the open countryside, was a formidable element in the changing scene of the nineteenth century. Rural estates, set apart in the age of exclusively horse driven transport, became readily available to the traveller. The man with money and a gun, and the ability to use it, identified himself with a new environment. The map of fashion underwent a profound change.

From medieval times large lumps of the country had been secret places. Few from the south ventured into the bulge of East Anglia, below the Wash, where King John lost his crown jewels in the mire. The marshlands of East Anglia were dominated by wild men on stilts, who were known as tigers and who counted the flatlands as their own.

The moors, fells and dales of Yorkshire, Northumberland and Lancashire were largely roadless. In the eighteenth century the visit of Dr Johnson and Mr Boswell to the Highlands of Scotland was rightly accounted a major adventure. In cities like Bath, Edinburgh and York, or in new-fangled towns like Brighton, although the journey by coach was uncomfortable enough, the extremities of the land were unconsidered.

It was only towards the middle of the nineteenth century that the aviary of Britain was discovered. The former wilderness was on the migratory line of millions of wildfowl. Pheasants and partridges were endemic to the marshlands. The northern moors produced the red grouse which were to become the most sought after game birds in the world.

The message came with the railways. Royalty led the way. In 1852, Queen Victoria and the Prince Consort built Balmoral, and conferred on the Scottish Highlands the accolade of Royal Deeside. The Prince of Wales, later King Edward VII, bought the East Anglian estate of Sandringham in 1862, and Norfolk was lifted into a royal county. The railway

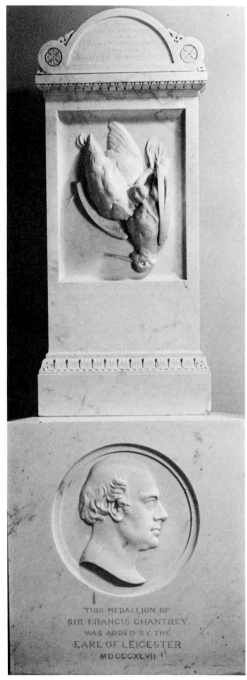

On November 20, 1829, Sir Francis Chantrey, the Victorian sculptor, killed two woodcock with one shot. Subsequently he presented his host with this souvenir attributing the feat as happening in 1830. Lord Leicester later added the medallion

A view of the royal estate of Sandringham
Sandringham in Norfolk is not the most handsome of English houses. But the 20,000 acre property, acquired by King Edward VII as Prince of Wales, is in the heart of the richest natural game country in England. No game is reared here. It is not necessary as the light, quickly draining soil is an ideal natural habitat.

companies provided stations at improbable places like the little village of Holkham in North Norfolk which was ornamented with an avenue of ilex, the Italian oak, to the great house. Sandringham too, had its own railway station, Wolverton. A royal train ran to Balmoral on Deeside. The secure dykes of the marshland gunners, the private hunting grounds of the stiltmen, and the heathered land of the Highland crofters were transformed.

A new world emerged. It was one, as Disraeli remarked, for the few and the very few. But it brought a new dimension into the countryside. Shooting game became a sport for the rich. Shooting game achieved the importance of a social accomplishment. A society came into being about country house parties, collected to shoot, which opened large parts of what had formerly been closed areas of Britain. It also happened, to the advantage of the human species, that the guests did not limit their shooting to the field. The coming of the shotgun, and the conviviality it encouraged, did much to improve the outward breeding of our own race.

There is little doubt that King Edward VII, mostly as Prince of Wales during Queen Victoria's long lifetime, contributed more than anybody to the making of shooting as a social occasion. Affectionately known to his contemporaries as 'Tum-Tum', he was dedicated to the sport. The hospitality he required reduced more than one of his hosts, among them Lord Walsingham, to bankruptcy. In fairness he probably did not realize the demands he made with his vast entourage on his faithful subjects.

A ridiculous extravagance attended the nineteenth-century shoots. Marquees were erected for luncheon. Four- and five-course meals were the order of the day. In the country house parties there was a procedure in which the women, after dressing for breakfast in modest tweeds, changed into wasp-waisted tea gowns and changed again into whispering petticoats and décolleté ball dresses for dinner. True the men themselves, when they came home from the field, had to change into tails and white waistcoats. The ceremony of life was ineluctable. In the evening the men played cards for small stakes before dinner and, after the ladies had left the table, for much higher ones.

The organisation of big shoots, up to the outbreak of the Kaiser's war, was formidable. It is no exaggeration to say that more than a hundred men were involved in arranging the pattern of the beats. The gamekeepers, who had reared the birds from the egg and put the poults into covert, were in charge. The big day was the test of their year's work.

On the great estates, they wore a distinctive uniform, a livery of silver buttons, buttoned leggings, red waistcoat and tweeds. At Holkham in North Norfolk, they wore the brown Coke bowler hat, adorned in the band with the pin-feathers of woodcock. It was a tradition that they were given a new suit of tweeds each year. The test of their skill was their capacity to show the birds over the guns on the big days in the coverts in November.

It has always been a harrowing job (it is no different now). On the day before the shoot the keepers had to mark, with an eye to the wind, how the driven birds would fly. They planted sticks, marked with numbered cards for the guns, red on the wrong side, white on the side where the guns were to stand. Often at dawn, on the day of the shoot, the keepers were out with the beaters blanking in the birds from what are called the 'outsides' into the home coverts.

A good keeper and his beaters pursued an art. His men were usually estate workers who knew the ground as well as he did. They were arranged strategically as stops on the flanks, pickers-up behind the guns, and dog-handlers to retrieve the fallen birds. The ambition of every keeper was to drive his birds over the guns as tall as he could and present them as few at a time as he could. In a covert crowded with pheasants there was a skill in tapping the trees with sticks making sure that not too many birds were in the air at the same time. The management of driven game was undoubtedly perfected, as it was invented, in the Victorian and Edwardian age. The system of driving birds is still followed in the field at the present time. What has largely changed is the attitude of shooting men themselves.

The people in the royalty-dominated world before World War I were unarguably a greedy lot. The nobility were selfish and self-satisfied. At best, they were not very nice to those whom they deemed their social inferiors, but kinder, perhaps, than their continental neighbours. Looking back, it is not easy, for instance, to respect the manners and the excesses of the shooting field before the lights went out in Europe. I cannot even claim that, as sportsmen, they were sporting. Perhaps they were the victims of a social system which was too rigid by half. Their sacrifices in the Great War showed that they did not lack sand. I can only report, of the few and the very few, how they were.

For the privileged, shotgun shooting became a way of life. It should be added that it made life fuller for lesser men within the law. 'Moleskins', the gamekeeper, assumed a social importance. Although he was abominably paid by modern standards, the gold sovereigns which were ribbed into his pockets by way of tips after a big day in the coverts were not contemptible. He was proud of his position. Even the beaters enjoyed what was for them a day out. They had beer, and bread and cheese, at luncheon, and mostly took home a brace of rabbits at the end of a day's shooting. The craftier ones knew how to kick a dead pheasant under a bramble for later collection. I am not at all sure that all the fun was on one side.

Indeed, I suspect that the discipline of the great shooting parties imposed more of a strain on the guns taking part than the horde of its attendants. Everybody's eyes were upon them. Outsiders, normally unwelcome, made a habit, especially when royalty was present, of shinning up trees to watch the sport. It was a pastime which was peculiarly prevalent in the coal mining areas of the North. Like football today, it provided an occasion for barracking.

The rules of the day were as strict as a game of cricket. When the guns assembled they made a draw for their numbered stands by picking out ivory tickets from a leather case. Their number was the number of the place they took on the first stand. Subsequently, the system was that they moved up two places on every stand which followed. Young men, serving their apprenticeship in the field, were not given numbers. They were appointed to back up the beaters and cover the flanks. Even the numbered guns were required on occasion to walk up with the beaters. Admittedly the rule was sometimes modified when royalty and crack shots were present. A card was issued telling each person, where they were to stand on each drive without respect for the luck of the draw. The captain of the shoot was anxious that royalty should be satisfied, and that the crack shots ensured a record bag.

A cavalcade of horse-drawn carts assembled to serve the party. An ammunition waggon, loaded with cartridge magazines, oak-lined, London leather finished and embossed with the initials or coronet of its owner, followed the guns. Another cart was equipped with racks to hang the pairs of pheasants, and other game, as they were brought in after each drive. Brakes were provided to move the guns from stand to stand.

The guns themselves, in the heyday of the Victorian and Edwardian shooting parties, were served by two loaders, and sometimes even a boy as well. On big days they shot with a matched threesome of guns. Changing guns was an art in itself. Without turning his head the gun had to rely on his loaders to press another into his hands. The loaders doubled up beside him as he shot to give him free range to swing his gun to right or left. The teamwork required was not easily achieved. The top shots practised with their men to achieve a perfection of gun passing. As a consequence, I believe it to be true that some of the top exponents, on days when the air was crowded with pheasants, could have four or five dead in the air at the same time. While I do not think that they were more skilful than contemporary game shots, they specialised in pace of gun-handling in an age when the size of the bag was a fetish.

It is said that, on major days at Holkham in Norfolk, the formidable Lord Leicester, the grandson of Thomas Coke, would not permit a shot to be fired during the morning when the guns and the beaters walked the birds into his main covet at Scarborough Wood. In the afternoon the guns were banked in three lines for the holocaust which followed.

The present head keeper at Holkham tells me that, when the birds were at last collected in the five-acre circle of Scarborough Wood crouching under an acre of laurel in the heart of it, the beaters stood back and the first of four keepers paced quietly into the covert. He was followed by the second, the third and the fourth. The art was to raise the birds over the bank of guns a few at a time. Only at the last of the drive, the line of beaters came in.

It was not all perfectly disciplined. It is told that on an important day on a drive at Scarborough, Lord Lewisham, afterwards Lord Dartmouth, had his gun taken away for 'acting like a clown'. The rules of the shooting field were already being firmly established.

It was often like that. I have heard of a drive of pheasants, in which a thousand birds were killed, during which the guns sent a message to the head keeper to stop it for a while, because their weapons were too hot to hold. The passing of that age is not to be regretted.

It is a fact that, in shotgun shooting, it was once fashionable to attempt records. Every landowner wanted to claim in his game book enormous bags. Many of them today are unbelievable.

To my mind the most remarkable performance was at Blenheim, the Duke of Marlborough's seat in Oxfordshire, on October 7, 1898. On that day five guns shot between them 6,943 rabbits, let alone 'the various'. The feat, as a mark of shooting skill, was not notable. Rabbits, stunk out of their burrows, are reasonably easy targets. But each gun shot over a thousand rounds. What is incredible is that they all claimed, at the end of the day, that none of them had a sore shoulder from recoil.

By general consent, Lord Ripon and Lord Walsingham were counted the best game shots of their age. It is said that Ripon, notably a dull dog in private life, once killed 28 pheasants in a minute. Lord Walsingham got himself into the record books when he killed to his own gun, and by himself, 1,070 grouse on Bluberhouse Moor on August 30, 1888. He had two lines of beaters driving the birds between the stem of an hour-glass line where he stood with his guns. In the end the birds were so tired that they could scarcely fly. It was a Pyrrhic victory.

It became fashionable to nominate the best game shots. Since they achieved little else, with the notable exception of Sir Ralph Payne-Gallwey who, as a writer and innovator, was altogether an unusual person, it is valueless to record their forgotten names. Out of wealth, and with an excess of leisure, they attained nothing which others with equal opportunities could have done just as well. The big shots were mostly unimportant people.

Under the over-riding rule of royalty, they were all conformists in the social scale. Their manners were determined by the clocks at Sandringham, where the hands were always set half-an-hour fast so that nobody would be late, and they were dominated by formidable old tyrants like the second Lord Leicester of Holkham, who commanded them about as he ordered his eighteen children. Game shooting, in what is generally regarded as its kingfisher days, was not the light-hearted affair it is sometimes supposed to have been. In many respects it was as tough as Caterham Barracks under the discipline of the Guards. Even 'Tum-Tum' required his guests to conform to the strict etiquette of his house, although it is

The bird museum at Holkham Hall contains a collection of all the species shot on the estate. This is only a fraction of it. Note the albino pheasant (*top left*) and the golden pheasant (*top centre*)

said that it was even more rigid in shooting parties at Windsor where foreign potentates were normally entertained.

For women in vast stately homes remote from shops and the fashionable roundabout it must have been alarmingly boring to be deserted for the first half of winter by their menfolk. True, there were retinues of servants to stoke the open fires in draughty places without central heating. They joined the guns for gargantuan breakfasts, served under batteries of silver, before the shooting party left for the field.

Traditionally they joined the guns at luncheon served in a marquee or lodge in the coverts. After lunch they stood behind the guns to watch the sport. A few, a very few, of the ladies went shooting themselves. Most hated those damp afternoons in which their voluminous skirts trailed in the mud and their top heavy hats swayed in the wind. They felt bound to applaud the prowess of the guns, dropping dead birds all about them, when all they really wanted was admiration for themselves.

At the end of the day it was the custom to arrange the bag in serried ranks for the gratification of the host and admiration of the guests. There was often a photograph taken of the entire party, including the ladies. Each gun was presented with a pair or two pairs of grace birds, as they were called, by the keepers. It provided the opportunity to pass a surreptitious sovereign or two by way of a tip. The tips were an important bonus to the keepers' wages. A gun who undertipped was a marked man on another shooting day.

The keepers and the beaters had their friends and enemies. No gun was more unwelcome than one who held up the order of the day by claiming imaginary lost birds and 'runners'. The keepers and beaters did not miss much of what went on. The dog-handlers, standing behind the guns, would mark the fallen. If a bird was lost they would pick it at their leisure at dawn the following morning. Meanwhile guns had to be positioned for the next drive. There was not a lot of daylight left.

Almost certainly the oldest game book in existence, and possibly the first ever made, dates from September 2, 1793 to October 9 1798. It was kept by Thomas Coke at Holkham in Norfolk on the suggestion of his political friend Mr C. J. Fox. So it is fair to claim that Charles James Fox, the great Whig statesman, was the orginator of the Game Book as we know it now.

A folio volume, bound in vellum, it records the numbers of game killed each day on the estate. Without reference to the names of the gunners, it lists to whom the bag was disposed. Among them is Sir Horatio Nelson, who on October 10, 1797 received 6 partridges, 2 pheasants and 1 hare; on November 3, 4 partridges, 2 pheasants and 2 hares; and who, incidentally, is legendarily reputed in Norfolk to have been a dangerous shot. Mr Fox, the Archbishop of Aix, the Duke of York and Dr Heath (headmaster of Eton) are amongst those who received game; plus the butcher, baker, grocer, postman, innkeeper, garden man and sundry farmers. No one was forgotten.

(*Opposite below*) **The first game book in existence**
It is said that the notion of keeping a game book was first suggested by Charles James Fox to his friend Lord Leicester. This list tells of the game killed at Holkham in October and November 1793; and to whom it was given away. The guns are not listed, although they were certainly among the recipients

GAME KILLED.

GAME KILLED.

In 1885 the game books record the performance of individual guns, listing what they claimed and the totals picked up by the keepers and the beaters. The custom was only dropped on the suggestion of the Duke of York (later George V). Now, on shooting days, only total bags are recorded

The greatest shot of his times
Lord de Grey, later Marquis of Ripon, was counted the greatest gameshot among 'the ten best shots in England'. De Grey, who kept up the practice of keeping a detailed list of the game he killed after 1913, bagged between 1867–95, 316,699 head including 111,190 pheasants, 89,491 partridges, 47,468 grouse. Up to his death he brought his total score to well over half-a-million

The largest total of partridges, in any one season, was 3,800 in 1797–8, and more than half the game killed seems to have been given away. In that season 2,322 partridges, 250 pheasants, 735 hares, 60 rabbits and 39 woodcocks were distributed as gifts out of the total bag of a little under seven thousand.

The second Game Book is a quarto volume, also bound in vellum, which deals with the period from September 1797 to December 1798. It now gives the names of the guns shooting each day, what they shot and the lists of presents given to local worthies. The search for record bags was on its way. Holkham has kept the record ever since.

In the middle of the nineteenth century it reached undue proportions. Between 1840 and 1859 the Hon Wenman Coke, a younger brother of the second Earl of Leicester, excusing himself that his performance with the gun excluded 1851–6 when he was absent from England on foreign travel and serving in the army in the Crimean War, kept a pocket diary of

(*Opposite*) **The heyday of driven gameshooting**
Lord de Grey shooting with three guns on the Earl of Pembroke's estate at Wilton near Salisbury. This action photograph must be one of the earliest ever recorded. Two of the round-actioned hammer guns, in frail condition after a lifetime of hard shooting, are still preserved by Purdey's the makers

his bag in the field. It was called *The Pocket Sized Game Book*. It listed the names of the principal London Gunmakers, dealers in firearms and gunpowder manufacturers. It is also detailed regarding his own achievements as a shot, all with a muzzleloader, over the years.

His claim is that he shot 12,627 head of game to his own gun over a period of little more than fifteen shooting seasons. In 1851 he records that he had never shot so well before: 176 pheasants, 431 partridges, 324 hares. Apart from hares and rabbits, partridges and pheasants, he killed blackcock and grouse, woodcock, snipe, plover and wildfowl. It makes even the lifetime bag of Colonel Peter Hawker seem relatively small.

Throughout the nineteenth century the count of personal achievement in the field was eagerly recorded. In the Holkham Game Books, it is told for posterity that on October 27, 1830, Master T. W. Coke (2nd Earl), then aged seven years, killed a hare running at full speed. On December 2, 1830, the young master felled a hen pheasant.

It was also a period in which bets were laid on the most trifling achievements. All the best London clubs had their betting books. At Holkham a guest bet Lord Coke on November 19, 1841, that he could not kill 35 snipe in any one day before November 26. Lord Coke won the bet. Lord Spencer bet Lord Coke on November 11, 1843, that he would not kill 70 rabbits in a day. Lord Coke killed 72.

The counting of individual scores and perhaps the excessive boasting that went with it, was brought to an end in Britain in 1900, although individual cards are still kept in continental Europe. It is said that the Duke of York (later King George V) suggested that it was inappropriate to make personal claims. Subsequently, even the Marquis of Ripon, counting his individual record up to half a million, closed his Game Book.

Two World Wars have destroyed a leisured generation which, in its stiff-necked way, created a social scheme for the privileged based on the amusement of the chase. The British have not lost their taste, inherited from Norman ancestors, for the pastimes of the field. What has changed are the people who take part in them.

In pockets, the old grace and favour shoots, cultivated by the great landowners of the past, still survive. They are becoming increasingly rarer. Great estates let out their lands to 'syndicates', a term describing an arrangement in which single guns join a party for a fee entitling them to eight or twelve shooting days in a season. From the Highlands of Scotland to the partridge manors of the South, shooting agents let out guns at prices reckoned on the potential size of the bag to those who are willing to pay.

Shooting in Britain has increasingly become the prerogative of successful industrialists and rich foreigners. The sport is none the worse, but the old landowners stay on the sidelines and collect the revenue from invaders. The exception is still the rough shoot where farmers entertain their friends in the traditional way. The cost of rearing game has risen so astronomically that paying guns have now become an essential part of the economics of great estates.

The luxury of the shooting week-end, the pavilioned luncheons, the white-tied and silken rustle of candlelit dinner parties have passed as surely as the entente cordiale of Edward VII. The shooting party is now, with rare exceptions, a commercial business.

On the obverse side of the royal coin it is proper to add that shooting today is friendlier and less snob-ridden than it used to be. The relation between shooters, gamekeepers and beaters is warmer. There is no longer the same rigid determination to collect vast bags.

A Norfolk farmer's shoot in 1943

'*Father was a gamekeeper and when he lost that job, he turned poacher in earnest. He had to, with eleven of us to feed. I began to learn from him early, as soon as I could walk far enough to go with him. When I was big enough to carry them I had to take the tools of his trade, his decoy birds, his nets and his cartridges . . . Father, as I have said, was a poacher, but he was a sportsman too . . . It was our wits and skill against the wild.*'

FRED J. SPEAKMAN
A Poacher's Tale (1960)

A Poaching Loafer.

CHAPTER 13

MOLESKINS AND HIS COVERTS

'Moleskins', the gamekeeper, got his nickname because traditionally his wife made him a waistcoat out of the skins of the moles he trapped on the land under his care. He dried the little skins on a board outside the hut in the woods where he kept his tools and the feed for his game. Before the days of the Land Rover his life was one of almost complete isolation. His transport, if he was lucky, was a pony and cart. His cottage was likely to be as remote as his hut.

Mellors, the keeper in *Lady Chatterley's Lover*, withdrawn in his green retreat, deeply resenting the blackness of industry all about him in the Midlands, is an authentic character. Keepers in the nature of their job have seldom been hail-fellow-well-met. In the past they certainly did not join in the convivialities with the locals in the village inns. Like Kipling's

153

The head keeper at Sandringham
Mr Montague Christopher, now in his seventh season at Sandringham numbers ten relations in a keepering family. He has twelve beat keepers, men and boys, to look after the estate. On the royal property no game is reared as it flourishes in a welcome environment

cat who walked by himself they never advertised their movements. Day and night, especially at night, they kept a wary eye on their coverts, and their neighbours.

Affrays between keepers and poachers were common. Murders were not unknown. A hidden war was waged unceasingly between the keepers and the night gunners, the long netters and the ne'er-do-wells setting snares for rabbits and hares, or baiting pheasants with a hook and a raisin.

It was customary to litter the fields with brambles, where the partridges jukked, to foul the nets of the poachers. In the full moon, when it was easy to pick off pheasants silhouetted against the bare branches of the winter trees, the keepers never slept.

Since the days of the Normans and Robin Hood, poaching has been a national pastime of the British. It is easier for keepers today with their vans, even two-way radios, to keep control in a society without the desperate poverty of the past; one indeed in which the majority of people have lost understanding of the ways of the countryside. Many do not recognise a

Where driven game shooting began
At Holkham Hall in North Norfolk the contemporary head keeper Mr James Preston stands beside the livery which keepers on the estate wore in the past. Traditionally the Coke hat, the bowler, is said to have got its name here. It is arguable. Another branch of the Coke family lived in Derbyshire. Perhaps that is why a bowler in America is still known as a Derby

The shoot of King Edward VII
As Prince of Wales, King Edward VII bought the 20,000 acre estate at Sandringham in 1882. His hope was to make it the best sporting estate in the country. 'Captain's Close' (seen in the background) was one in which the guns walked out the birds, taking their stand for the drive out of 'Fox Covert' (to the right). Enormous bags have been taken here

(*Opposite*) **Thomas Coke of Norfolk**
Coke's friend Thomas Gainsborough painted this life-sized portrait—it is said to have been Gainsborough's last—in 1782. It was painted at Holkham when Coke was in his twenties. The dogs at Coke's feet are believed to have been the forbears of the Gordon Setter.

GAME KILLED.

1875	By whom Killed.	Partridges.	Pheasants.	Hares.	Rabbits.	Wood Cocks	Snipes.	Ducks.	Teal.	Various.	Tot.	
		272	13	1221	569	15	100	7	7	23	3110	
Dec 14	Maharajah Duleep Sing	3	215	44	2	3					267	Dec.
	Hon. E. Digby	.	31	56	1	1					89	
	Lord E. Cavendish	1	180	43	.	.					224	
	Lord Leicester		5	1	.	.					6	
	Lord Clinger	1	61	56	1	1					120	
	Hon. W. Coke		13	2	.	.					15	
	Lord Ruthven	.	56	61	4	2					123	
	Mr. Birkbeck	1	111	47	1	3	.			.	163	
	Captain Vivian		107	56	1	1	.	.		.	165	
	Lord Powerscourt	2	32	82	.	2	.			.	118	
	Lord Dacre		42	38	.	.					80	
	Lord Coke	2	37	57	1	2	.		.		99	
	Claimed	10	840	543	11	15	.	.	.		1466	
	Returned	11	904	634	15	16					1580	
15	Keepers				4	3					7	

The most famous game covert in the world
It looks empty here. Scarborough Wood, a five-acre spinney (on the right) part of the Holkham estate, is the place where beaters and guns collected pheasants throughout a morning's walk. Thousands of birds crouched under the laurels in the core of the spinney at Scarborough Stop. Huge bags were taken by the lines of guns who stood to the right outside the photograph

gamebird when they see one. But the poacher, nowadays more often in a car with a .22 rifle, still haunts the fringes of the coverts. Game grows increasingly more valuable in the commercial market. The keeper's job, keeping the birds safe and together, is still one of wary watchfulness. His new enemies are yobbos, without any knowledge of the field, who create damage for the hell of it. Instant transport in motor cars provides them with the means.

A head keeper for forty years, Frank Hart, the son of a head keeper on the same estate, administers a shoot with five beats and four underkeepers. In the south of England he is counted the doyen of his craft

Game-rearing is not quite the same laborious process that it was in the past. Modern methods have largely mechanised the system. Few game birds today are hatched in the old-fashioned way under broody farmyard hens. Modern hybrid fowls seldom become broody at all. Now mere egg-laying machines, they have lost the maternal instinct. The incubator is now the foster mother of game. A breeding stock of hen birds, to provide the next season's eggs, is penned before shooting begins. In open enclosures the wild cocks seek them out for fertilisation. Even grey partridges, which for long defeated the game rearers, are now responding to largely artificial conditions. Much is now artificial. The keeper is not helped by modern farming systems, far more efficient in production than any in the past, which are not friendly to the wild stock on the ground. It is a paradox that game, notably the partridge, thrives on poor weed-infested land.

The hard labour of keepering is game-rearing and vermin control. The high art of it is in the presentation of birds over the guns. If the drives go awry on a shooting day the rest of the year's work has been a waste of money and time. The challenge is that every estate and manor has its own idiosyncrasies and presents its own problems. The keeper has to plan his tactics—different keepers have different styles—like a general in the field. His manoeuvres call for the disciplined control of a line of stops and beaters; and, not least, the disciplining of his guns.

In the rolling chalklands of Berkshire the pheasant-shooting at Yattendon is exceptional. In the days of the late Lord Iliffe, the father of the present owner, a thousand pheasants were killed in a season. Today, Mr Hart rears nine thousand for largely syndicate shoots

Mr Douglas Bowler, head keeper outside the pavilion on the cricket ground at Hackwood Park. The mock Palladian building is used for luncheon on shooting days

The centres of any shoot are the home coverts in which the birds are fed and raised. In the early part of the season the 'outsides' are driven with the intention of pushing the birds home. At the height of the season in November, when the main harvest of game is collected, the birds in the home coverts are guided hopefully over the guns to adjoining ones, and then brought back again. The tactic is made possible by the general pattern of small woods, spinneys, marl pits and roots in the English country scene. When the birds are flushed they can see within easy reach of their flight the next point of refuge.

The ideal is to place the guns between them at fixed points where the contours of the land, and the height of the trees, ensures that they fly as tall and fast as possible. In coverts crowded with pheasants it is also important to prevent them all taking wing at the same time.

Unruly beaters can spoil a year's work in the coverts. Beaters, under the firm control of a good keeper, make the bag. You may judge how well, or badly, a shoot is run by the quiet, or the lack of it, in which the beaters do their work. The gentle tapping of sticks on the tree trunks is a sign of efficiency. Beaters are traditionally only supposed to raise their voices with the call of 'cock-up' when a woodcock is sighted in the rides.

The keeper must essentially be a keen observer of his charges' comforts. Every estate has its cold places which pheasants avoid. There is not enough warm cover, a lack of wild berries, foliage which has grown too rank and tall, or just something which only a pheasant would know about. Throughout the year, with hook and scythe, the keeper must look for the answer. After the outbreak of myxomatosis the ecology of the country underwent a

Hackwood, the historic property in Hampshire owned by Viscount Camrose and Colonel the Hon Julian Berry, is famous as a sporting estate because its 4,000 acres were laid out in 1937 by the first Lord Camrose as a haven for game. The coverts, unusually, are not named but are numbered one to nine.

The traditional 'Moleskins'

From the end of the eighteenth century to the twentieth, the figure typifies the pattern of the man who emerged with the evolution of sporting arms. John Buckle, head keeper at Merton, Norfolk, in the eighteen-eighties, was the grandson of 'Old' Watson who died in 1834, the son of Israel Buckle who died in 1873. Between them they spanned the development of the game gun from the flintlock to breechloader, from pot-shooting to the days of the huge bags. John Buckle is wearing velveteens, moleskin waistcoat, buttoned leggings and hard hat which was the uniform of a keeper of the time. He carries a long barrelled hammer gun, with Damascus barrels

163

profound change. Without the rabbits to nibble down the rank growth in the woods the undercover grew so thick that the pheasants were unmanageable. They had shelter from which they could not be dislodged.

Every man who uses a shotgun should recognise what he owes to the gamekeeper. It is less a job than a calling, demanding unearthly hours of work through about eleven months in the year (February is the keeper's holiday time) and a dedication which is denied to any but a true country lover. Not surprisingly, it extends through generations. Gamekeepers marry into gamekeeping families. I could not have written much of this book without the friendships I have shared with them.

'Nobody expects to play golf well without proper coaching and regular practice. Yet, although 'swing' is as important in game gun shooting as it is in golf, and although there are other notable similarities in the two sports such as, for example, the prime necessity of keeping your eye on the object you are aiming to hit, most men who get an occasional day with a gun are disappointed with themselves because they fail to put up a good performance. The secret of straight shooting, like playing scratch golf, is constant practice, a steady temperament and a knowledge of the game.'

ROBERT CHURCHILL

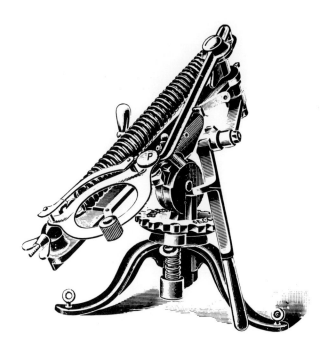

CHAPTER 14

THE SHOOTING SCHOOL
AND SHOOTING FIELD

THE SHOOTING SCHOOL

It was not until 1925, more than a generation after the breechloading, self-ejecting, double-barrelled gun had come into general use, that a brief textbook was published under the name of Robert Churchill, the London gunmaker, called *How To Shoot*. In fact the book was 'ghosted' by Major Hugh B. C. Pollard who, a year later, published his classic *History of Firearms*. Thirty years on I myself wrote the greatly enlarged *Churchill's Game Shooting*. The pioneer work written by Pollard, the more extensive one revised in many subsequent editions by me, combined with the practical teaching of Churchill himself, constituted the first serious attempt to rationalise the science of game gun practice.

Undoubtedly the best shots of Victorian and Edwardian times were superb exponents of the art. The vast bags they killed are evidence of that. But none of them explained effectively how they did it. I suspect that most of them at the country house parties were an unin-quisitive, perhaps unintellectual lot. After Colonel Peter Hawker only Sir Ralph Payne-

165

The late Norman Clarke, Shooting Coach of Churchill's and Holland & Holland

Gallwey, a dedicated naturalist in the rather ruthless Victorian interpretation, made a serious attempt with his *High Pheasants in Theory and Practice* to explain the skills of the sport.

The crack shots of his time were natural shots because, if they were not, they would not have been invited to the great days in the coverts, in the partridge manors, and on the moors. They shot well because they fired ten thousand and more cartridges in a season. Even a modest shot can improve his performance enormously if he shoots as prodigiously as that. The secret of 'the best shots in England' was that they scarcely did anything else except shoot from August to January. A fellow with only the chance of a couple of shots in a day could not expect to compete with them, even if he wished to.

Robert Churchill once said to me, recalling the vast shoots of the past: 'It does not matter if you miss the first six pheasants of the day. Make sure you get one partridge before you attempt a brace. Don't worry if you miss the first grouse in the first drive.' I reminded him that, in most of my shooting, that was all we saw in a day. He replied correctly, that that is why you need to run yourself in on clay pigeons in a shooting school.

The shooting school, with clay discs catapulted into the air out of spring traps, was a latecomer in the development of the shotgun. It provides a test of marksmanship, under artificial conditions, which is still the best way, outside the field, of learning to shoot straight. Unhappily, like most schooling these days, it is expensive. But there is no more certain way of improving performance. The coaches in the shooting schools have ways of throwing easy targets which can encourage the most despondent shot. They can excite him until he can

The "Bogardus" Trap.   The Blue Rock Pigeon.   The "Carver" Revolving Trap.

smash clays out of tall towers which are really good ones. I doubt if any coach today instructs in the clumsy language of an earlier generation.

The notion of shooting at flying and running game that used to be expounded was based on a theory of making a forward allowance to allow for the speed of the quarry. The system, as I shall show, is essentially unworkable in practice.

In the past, gunhandling and footwork were only vaguely defined. I have noticed wood-cuts of supposedly correct positions in early books on shooting which almost certainly ensured a miss. The nearest that Hawker, Payne-Gallwey and Walsingham got to the grammar of the thing was to insist, quite rightly, on the absolute necessity of trigger-pressing (not pulling, please) at the instant that the butt of the gun is bedded into the shoulder. In their way and in their day they did it well. The modern shotgunner is advised to consider other factors.

Unlike the rifle, in which a steady slow-breathing aim is so important, a shotgun is a weapon of movement. Although it is the custom to put a bead on the end of game gun barrels, you may depend upon it that if you see the sight or, indeed, hear your gun go off when you shoot at a moving target, you will almost certainly miss. The reason is the same reason which confounds a golfer when he takes his eye off the ball. You cannot afford to avert your concentration away from the target.

The logic of it is that if you raise your index finger to point out an object in the landscape, your first point, because your eyes have to meet your finger, will be dead on. It is only if you keep pointing, that your eye and finger will lose correlation, and you will be all over the place. Hence the importance of the first lesson that a shotgunner, using his gun like an extension of his own arm, must shoot the instant the butt presses into his shoulder. It is fatal to look down the barrels, or even notice that they exist. You must fix your eye on the target, any part of it. The pattern of a shotgun charge is generous enough to cover feather or fur if you only concentrate on a wing, a leg, or a beak. If you are conscious of anything beyond the target do not be surprised if it passes without a feather or a fleck of fur in disarray.

Good shots are never in a hurry when they sight game. The secret is a slow lift and a quick finish. For a tall pheasant, it was once said to me that, as you lift your gun, you have always time to say 'What a beautiful fellow you are' before you touch the trigger. I myself have found it helps, when I am off form, to make myself angry with an expletive. It concentrates the mind.

Nothing that I have written so far is valuable without a conscious understanding of the correct positions in shotgun shooting for hands, head and feet. The first consideration is to

167

make yourself one with your gun. You need to use it, if you are going to use it successfully, as an extension of your own body.

It is, of course, important that your gun fits you. Young men, with lithe frames, find it easier to modify themselves to a bad gun fit. Young men can look good in clothes which would shame a middle-aged one. But both will shoot better with guns made to the owner's measure, as London guns should be, and usually are. If you pick up second-hand ones they can be modified.

The athletics of shooting—and, make no mistake, to shoot two partridges in front, change guns and shoot two behind is a feat comparable with a boundary in first class cricket—requires a conscious concentration on style. I have condensed here what I believe to be the essential concomitants of safe, straight and tidy shooting.

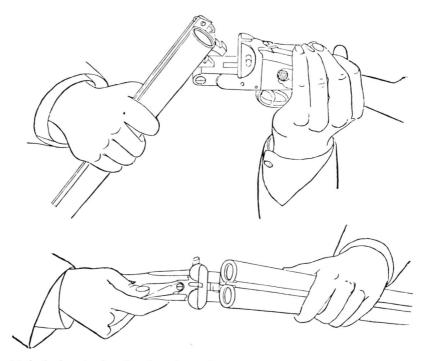

Method of putting barrels and stock together

How to put a gun together

It occurs to me that this book may easily fall into the hands of a young man who has been presented with his first gun. In his haste to use the gun he can so easily damage it. I am afraid that some older men are not without guilt either. So this is the first rule. When you take a good gun out of its leather case, a gun which costs an awful lot of money, lift it out of the baize with two fingers sunk into the muzzles of the barrels. Normally the fore-end is attached to the barrels. Most people, when they remove it, put it on one side as they hook on the lumps of the barrels to the action. *Don't*!

The proper method, when you release the fore-end is to lift it back in front of the loops of the barrels, holding it in place until you engage them in the action of the gun. With the stock firmly held under your arm, present the barrels to it at a full right angle. Draw them gently over the hooks in the face of the action. Make sure that you are holding the top lever of the gun at full pressure before you lift.

If you handle old guns you will soon discover how often the metal has been bruised on the hinge by careless assembly. Bring the three components of the gun together unhurriedly, and affectionately. It is a fit which can be conducted without manual effort. When the barrels have locked into place, clip the fore-end back into position. That may sound unimportant but the value of a gun depends on attention to details like that.

Loading cartridges into the breech

At this stage it might seem unimportant to discuss cartridges in bags. It is not. In rough shooting, where shots are infrequent, cartridge belts and bandoliers of one sort or another are favoured (see Chapter 17). In driven gameshooting, with one gun or two, a cartridge bag is essential. The first thing to know before shooting begins is to give the bag, or your pocket a good shake. The shaking has the effect of encouraging the cartridges, which are lead heavy with the weight of shot at the point of closure, to tipple over so that the brass bases come quickly to hand. The matter is one of some importance in a hot corner.

When you break your gun to eject the fired cases, your hand should be on the way to your pocket or bag at the same time. If you have shaken well, the brass ends will come to your fingers easily. Take two cartridges and, as you collect them in your hand, make a movement of your fingers to ensure that the lower one is more prominent than the top one by about three-quarters of an inch; in other words, pick them out in an over-and-under position. Insert the nose of the under cartridge into the right barrel but don't let go of it. Using it as an axis, twist your wrist so that the other cartridge turns over the left barrel. Let both go and you will load at speed without barking your knuckles.

The system should be rehearsed in dry practice with dummy cartridges called snap-caps. *Never*, repeat *never*, pull the trigger on an empty gun. It jars, and can severely damage the action.

I am here only briefly repeating the system of shooting which Robert Churchill taught and which I have explained in greater detail in other books. But this history of the shotgun would be incomplete without the essential elements of the discipline which Churchill advocated. Nobody today, although it came as a surprise in 1925, is essentially in disagreement with his teaching. Out of compliment to his memory. I have used the photographs of him demonstrating correct shooting style when he was in his prime.

The safety factor

In every textbook on game gun shooting there is an emphasis placed on the dangers that the sport involves in careless hands. While disagreeing with none of it, an experienced shot is entitled to make personal exceptions in the rules of the game.

For instance, it is theoretically correct that the safest way to carry a gun is in the shoulder-arms position. In practice the most convenient way is to carry it in the crook of the arm.

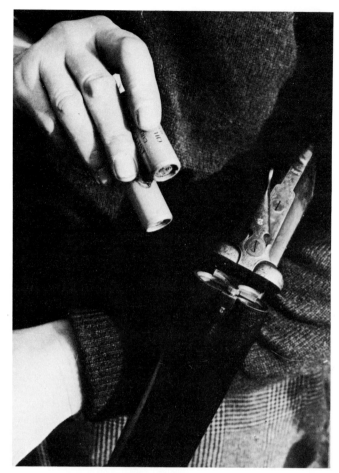

How to pick up two cartridges for ease of loading

With the barrels open, it is the most comfortable method and everybody can see, between drives, that the gun is unloaded. Churchill had a habit, when he was demonstrating a weapon, of breaking it and offering the barrels for inspection. 'Empty' he would say loudly before he showed how the gun should be used.

Every modern gun has a catch below the top lever marked 'safe'. It is an unfortunate word which might well be replaced by 'check' which would explain more exactly what the lever does to contain the triggers when the gun is loaded. It is never safe. Neither will it help you to shoot well. The teaching which advises to keep on 'safe' until you lift the gun to your shoulder is doubling the risk of a miss. You have two matters to think about when one is quite enough. If, in looking for game, you push forward your safety-catch, hold your gun at a correct angle and lift it into your shoulder with your trigger finger laid protectively over the guard, you will be a better shot. I often wonder whether the safety catch is viable at all. King George V, a dedicated shot, insisted on using hammer guns with a self-ejecting mechanism all his life. He reckoned that he could see what he was doing. He himself mistrusted the little slide marked 'safe'.

Hands: The ready position

When the gun is mounted Churchill recommended a system of what he called 'dry practice'. The first rule was to tuck the stock well in under the arm. He emphasised that a slack hold invited a miss. What he recommended was a confident squeeze. You must not be taut so that you sacrifice smoothness of action. He put it thus:

> I want you to tuck the stock under your own arm because (1) I want you to push your left arm forward as you mount, not merely raise it. (2) I want you to push your left arm forward because I am going to show you that the left hand is the aiming hand. (3) By pushing your left hand into the aim, you take a proportion of the recoil of the charge through your left arm and thence to your body rather than take it all on the shoulder. (4) In squeezing the gun under your armpit you are taking some of the weight off your hands and encouraging the muscles in your arms to relax. (5) The method will train you to put your shoulder to the stock instead of making the common error of putting the stock to the shoulder. (6) It is the quickest form of gun-mounting because the butt simply slips from the under-arm to the shoulder without losing contact with your body (that is important) and the gun comes easily and smoothly to eye-level. (7) The gun comes up to your face instead of the head going down to meet the stock, and faulty head movement is one of the commonest causes of poor shooting. (8) The system checks hasty gun-mounting, and encourages correct timing. (9) It prevents the incidence of bruised cheek and jawbone from the recoil. (10) It encourages the right hand to adopt the correct position on the side of the stock and so prevent a bruised middle finger. (11) It not only keeps you squarely on to your target (as your body is checked from turning too much sideways) but it also encourages you to adopt a natural stance. (12) Finally it encourages you to start your body swing whilst the gun is coming up.

Thus Churchill, laying down the law of shotgun shooting in his own idiosyncratic way, undoubtedly invented the logic of the art. Quietly he would not be denied any of the answers. I wrote so many words for him that I have no difficulty in expressing his theories of shotgun shooting here. He would approve.

Feet: The right position

Holding a weapon in your hands is only the first stage in good gunmanship. In game gun shooting stance is as important as it is in golf. Indeed, the position of your feet, like the importance of keeping your eye on the ball, is just the same. The swing and balance in straight shooting is the same as that demanded in golf. It is fortunate that, in shooting, middle-aged men who have the art can still compete with their juniors. If they have the legs, older men can sometimes shoot better, shooting more wisely, than the youngsters. Like the art of casting a fly in fishing, the skill lasts until you drop off the hook.

You will notice in the field that experienced shots stamp out the ground about them while they wait for a drive to begin. The art is to put your feet in the right place. It is peculiarly

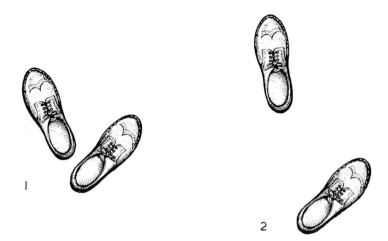

Fig 1 (Wrong). The diagram demonstrates the common fault of standing with heels too close together. The result is that the bulk of the recoil is taken by the shoulder without assistance from the legs. A frequent cause of bruised cheek and bruised second finger.

Fig 2 (Wrong). Right foot immediately behind left. This twists the body in such a way that the gunstock is not firm to the shoulder. The butt carries away to the arm muscles. The most frequent cause of second barrel misses.

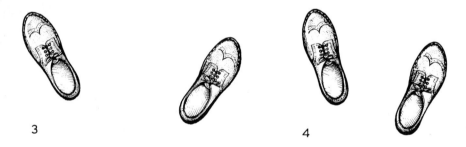

Fig 3 (Wrong). The stance is too wide. The shooter is unable to transfer body weight smoothly from one foot to the other. On uneven ground the recoil can even knock you over.

Fig 4 (Correct). The balance and poise of the body is even. Weight can be transferred from left to right, or right to left, and behind, and recoil is absorbed into your whole frame rather than the shoulder.

172

easy to adopt a bad style. The essential principle is that you must stand square to the gun. With one leg drawn back, the way novices are inclined to shoot, you will be off-balance. You must settle yourself to meet the recoil of the gun so that it passes comfortably down your legs.

The right position, although it varies with the shooter's height, is that the toes of his feet should be about 9in apart and his heels about 3in apart. It is better to take too narrow a stance than too wide a one. I have used line drawings here because they demonstrate simply the right and the wrong way to stand to a gun.

I appreciate that it is mildly irritating to be asked to practice 'muscle memory' without firing the gun. It is basically important. With your gun in your hands in 'the ready position', you should practise the swing from left to right, and right to left, and overhead, varying the balance on your legs, until, like the conductor's baton, you have moved into an easy rhythm. If you find yourself trying too hard you will certainly miss.

Left Hand Grip

The right and left hands should each do an equal share of the work of mounting the gun to the shoulder. The correct point of reach is found by balancing the gun between the two hands until the point of equal distribution of weight is found. If the left hand is too far back the stock will mount earlier than the barrels, which will 'sag'; also the recoil will be felt more heavily on the shoulder. If the left hand is too far forward the barrels will come up before the stock. This is almost as bad. The gun should be balanced to encourage horizontal mounting so that, by the time the butt touches the shoulder, the barrels should be pretty well parallel to the line set by the eyes. The left thumb should not be curled round the barrels but held lengthwise and made to project or, at least, be noticeable. This serves a double purpose for it cuts out disturbance of aim due to left eye vision and also prevents the fingers covering too much of the barrel and encroaching on the sighting nib. It also prevents the barrels jumping out of hand on recoil; another cause of a bruised cheek. While lifting the gun the barrels should only be held lightly, but should be gripped at the instant of firing.

You may adopt a correct stance and you may also take a perfect grip of the gun, yet you can still miss certain birds if your body or legs are wrongly braced. The perfect shotgun action is a smooth gradual mounting culminating in rigidity at the moment of recoil. (The left-shouldered shot, like myself, must obviously reverse these instructions.)

Gun-mounting: Position of the head

If you are less than disciplined in your drill in stance, footwork and grip, your gun-mounting will provide the critical test of your aim. It also involves not only your legs and your hands but your head. Indeed it is said that lazy head movement is the cause of one-half of the misses in shotgun shooting. You have to bring every limb into sympathetic movement with the gun.

Theoretically, if you are well-balanced on your legs, if you line your left index finger like a pointer over the barrels of the gun, if you thrust your shoulder purposefully into the stock, and if you touch off the triggers the moment the gun butts your shoulder, with your eyes not on the barrels but the target, you should never miss. In practice none of us can achieve that desideratum every time. If we could, the sport of shooting would not be worth bothering with. The important thing to know is not merely how to hit but why we miss. You should always recognise where you went wrong.

I have endeavoured here to compose a list of the mistakes we all make:

(1) The most common one, endemic in anxious shots, is to point the shotgun as if it were a rifle. If you see your barrels, that is if you have taken your eyes off the target, you have missed.

(2) I fancy that bad footwork is the second most serious fault. If you are caught off balance, or worse still, if you falter as you fire, your gun cannot help you. Balance has to be cultivated and that is why dry practice is so important.

(3) You have a sloppy head. You are putting down your head to meet the stock instead of allowing the stock to meet your head. You are not holding the muscles of your neck rigidly enough. A short stocky man is less liable to this fault than a tall thin one. But it is fatal for successful shooting. A palliative like an elastic band held between the teeth may help. But the correct cure is to practice lifting your gun to a stiff neck. The best position for the head is fairly erect and turned very slightly to the right.

(4) You are not using your hands to present your gun like an extension of your own arms. Your left index finger is not pointing up the gun on target. Your fingers are not leaving sufficient daylight behind the guard. If you bruise your second finger it is your own fault, and you are unlikely to shoot so confidently as the next bird comes over.

(5) You are 'pulling' the triggers. Your shoulder, as the butt of the gun is thrust home, should time the touch you put on the trigger. Think to yourself that the pressure of your oncoming shoulder really fires the gun. The more exactly you can make the two movements simultaneously the better you will shoot.

(6) You cannot train yourself not to miss. You should always know why you missed. An experienced gun when he is shooting ought to be able to say, 'I was over the top of that one', 'I was behind' or whatever. The ability to analyse a miss is a very important step in becoming a competent shot.

The theory of allowance

If you follow the instructions in the earlier part of this chapter and if you go to Shooting School which is the quickest way of all to learn straight shooting, this tailpiece is irrelevant. But shooting men, as I have discovered over the years, are sceptics. I am afraid that there are still those, even shooting coaches, who use that misleading word 'lead' to describe how they intercept moving targets at varying angles. It is one which ought to be excised from the shotgun dictionary. It misleads far many more people than it helps.

The 'allowance' principle, when allowed to enter shooting as an abstraction, is quite unsuited to the average sportsman, and if imperfectly understood, is a prolific source of irritation and error.

Pollard, who was a scientist as well as a ballistician, pointed out that a charge of shot takes $^1/_{20}$sec to travel 20yd; $^1/_{10}$sec, 30yd; $^1/_{7}$sec, 40yd. A bird travelling at 40mph covers 1, 2 or 3yd respectively in the same intervals, ($^1/_{20}$, $^1/_{10}$, and $^1/_{7}$sec) and we know that the gun must be pointed those distances ahead to score a kill. It is hopeless to attempt to calculate precise allowances for various ranges in the heat of shooting. The dead reckoner, the computer if you like, is the eye.

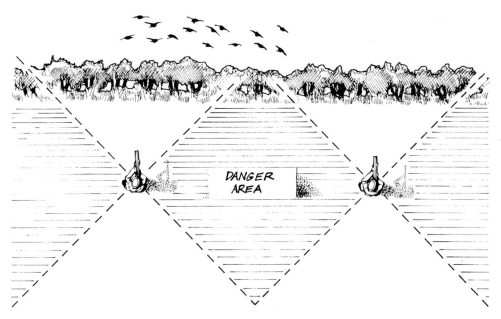

The legitimate field of fire

This diagram underlines the rules of safety and etiquette in all forms of shotgun shooting. It concerns driven birds but, walking up, the order is not so much different. It is assumed that guns are standing 30yd apart and well back from a hedge during a partridge drive. The legitimate fields of fire (the white area) for each gun are 90° in front and 90° behind. The shaded portions are the danger zones. Above all, the shooter must train himself, as a matter of safety, never to follow through into the shaded area. Whilst turning to shoot behind, the gun should be down from the shoulder and the barrels pointing skywards during the 90° traverse of the danger zone. As a matter of etiquette in the safety zones, especially when pheasants are flushed, you should hold your shot if a low bird looks likely to fly better for your neighbours. Ground game should never be shot in the danger zone. It is safer to take them behind

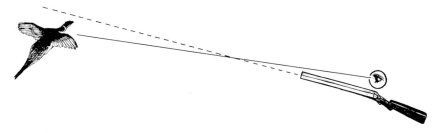

How it works
The theory of allowance by eye

The shooter's eye is fixed on the bird. He does not see his barrels. But the angle of the barrels of the gun as the butt is bedded into the shoulder makes the necessary forward allowance at the moment when trigger-pressing brings both together. Thus, if the head is held correctly, the necessary forward allowance is automatically provided for. The eye, like the first point of an index finger, is never wrong.

175

Allowance is needed, but it is no business of your brain. The secret is to regularize your movements and mount the gun properly to your shoulder so that hands and eye co-ordinate. Your barrel must always be aligned precisely where your eye is looking. The eye knows its job exactly. Apparently you are shooting straight at the bird but, unconsciously, you will be making all forward allowances. Practise the pointing of the left hand and body at the bird from the 'ready' position until you are doing it instinctively.

The difference between shooting at birds overhead and crossing, as compared with going-away, is that, besides being in more rapid flight, their line of travel is more or less at right angles to the line of fire. Therefore, theoretically, the gun must be directed further ahead than the going-away bird. Forget it. Keep your eye on the bird, and stick to gun-mounting drill. The more rapid gun movement, caused by the body swing if you have your eyes stuck on target, will automatically carry the aim further forward. If you mount your gun at a speed equal to the bird; in other words, if you keep your left hand pointing at the bird during the whole of the gun-mounting, then, if it is a slow incomer, the unconscious overthrow is very slight, but all that is needed for correct forward allowance. On the other hand, if it is a very fast crossing shot, your own speed is increased; the overthrow is proportionately greater and is, again, the correct forward allowance. If your technique is correct you will find that the right-angle target presents no difficulties.

Do not, whatever you do, mount the gun, and then swing. You will 'lead' correctly if you follow the drill. If you start thinking on it you will 'lead' all wrong.

This chapter would be inadequate if it concluded without adding that not all contemporary shooting coaches are in complete agreement with Churchill's method of teaching. The principles are generally accepted. Subsequently, experts like the late Percy Stanbury of the West London Shooting Grounds, have taught in a different manner. Stanbury argued that it was best to keep your feet square on the ground, without the foot movements of golf, and concentrate on a swing from the waist. It is a style more suited to a taller slimmer man than one of Churchill's stocky figure.

Different styles suit different people. At the end of the line, once you have mastered the essential elements of shotgun drill, in whatever school you learn it, you will develop a personal style of your own in just the same manner that a fly fisherman, once he has learnt the elements of his craft, does not have to think on it. He has 'muscle memory'. For good shooting your eye should be focussed, to the exclusion of every other factor, on the target. But you cannot exclude sweet body movement whether it is from your feet or your waist.

(Opposite) Tall pheasants

Shooting tall fast pheasants is an art which defeats all but the most experienced shots. The average pheasant, even though he tops well-grown oaks, is probably not more than 25yd high, while the vast majority of driven birds are barely 20yd high. A really high pheasant finds his 'ceiling', or extreme shootable range, at a vertical height of 44yd. He is still within range of your gun.

In the diagrams the squares represent 10yd in each dimension and the line in the angle of vision is taken as 45°. In the case of a bird flying on the 20yd height level it cuts the line of vision about 30yd from the gun while the bird on his 40yd height level comes into view nearly 60yd away. The low bird has only 20yd to travel before he is overhead, the high bird has 40yd to cover before he is over the guns. The questions of height and distance are deceptive. The higher bird seems to be travelling at half the speed of the lower bird. Distance is easy to misjudge

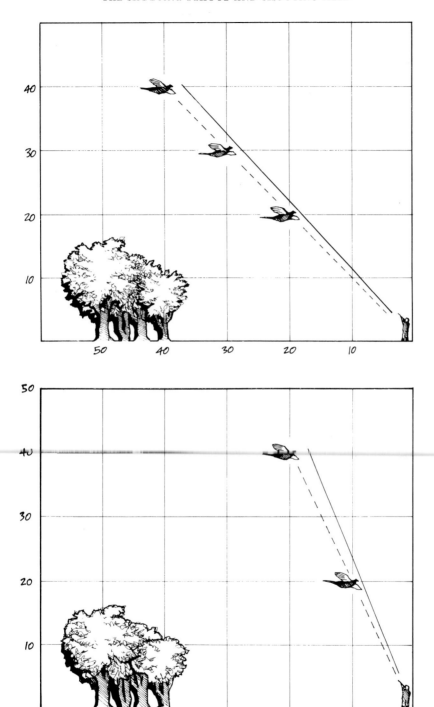

THE SHOOTING FIELD

The shooting school is the ideal preparation for the realities of the field. Clay pigeons tone gun-handling, bodywork and muscles. But it would be idle to pretend that a man who can 'kill' ten out of ten inanimate objects sprung out of a trap can be relied upon to put up the same sort of performance at game. The clay disc has a predictable arc. The line of flight, however skilfully the trapper varies the targets, is constant. The clays start fast, make a consistent curve, and fall slowly. Game, for the best of reasons, is not so accommodating.

I once invited a shooting coach, the best I have known at clay pigeons on his own patch, to join me in a pheasant shoot. He was bewildered. The targets came over, not in answer to a whistle, but surprisingly at their own speeds and angles. I fancy that he was also overwhelmed that his eye was filled, not with a little black disc, but the whirring excitement, the coloured glory of a cock pheasant breaking covert. In his own environment he could demonstrate to a keen novice the correct techniques of shooting in every situation. In the pheasant's own environment, in the challenge of the field, it was a different story.

I have seen the same thing happen with many Americans, who are masters of skeet shooting, a game in which most English shots are not in the same class. In Southern Africa I myself have even made something of an impression on Dutch farmers, who galloping on horseback could bring down a buck with a rifle, by shooting two tall duck with a right and a left. It is a matter of what you are used to.

The peculiarity of shotgun shooting in Britain is that, although the game offers no danger as it does in wilder climates, it has a charisma of its own. There is an eerie magic waiting in a partridge, pheasant or grouse drive before the birds come over. It is partly a matter of scenery when the harvest is in and the purple bells are whispering in the heather, and also the anticipation of the sudden explosion of birds, so often unexpected, which catches a man off his feet. It is a test of nerve.

Nobody seems to escape it. I recollect an anecdote of one of the crack shots of the Edwardian period being caught late at night in the library of the stately home where he was staying practising with his two loaders the art of exchanging guns. Gun fever, the anxiety that makes you miss, is a common one.

No doubt the correct attitude in the field is one of nonchalant attention. It is not easy to achieve. Oddly enough it is probably most helpful to be less eager than the rest of the guns. I have fond memories of a courtier, who, in the presence of royalty, after His Royal Highness had missed twice, raised his hat and, making his excuses, killed the great man's two birds behind.

In the ultimate reckoning the art of shooting is never to get excited, or over-eager. It is an axiom that, if you are well-skilled in gun-handling, the less you try the better you will shoot.

A complete understanding of gun manners in the field will make you more welcome. It is essential that you understand the rules of shooting. In a line of guns you should only shoot at birds within your own arc of fire. If they are clearly flying to your neighbour, and they may be better birds for him, manners require you to hold your hand. I recall an occasion when I stood beside a captain of the Surrey cricket team who knocked off every bird, right and left, as if he was fielding in the slips. He was very good in his way, but he was not invited again.

It is sometimes acceptable, among close friends, to agree to poach each other's birds. I

Dry Practice: Partridge Shooting: 'Fire'
Starting from the ready position, the exercises should be followed, gun in hand, in dry practice with snap caps

Turn, with a pivot of the right toe, to take a forward partridge, left

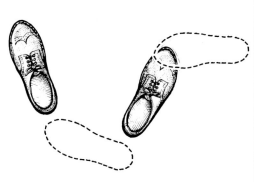

Make an almost complete turn to take a back partridge, left

Make a reverse turn to take a forward
partridge on the right

Swing round as far as you can to take a
back partridge on the right

Dry Practice: Tall Pheasants: 'Fire'
The weight is on the right foot to take a high
pheasant on the right. Note that the whole body
shapes like an additional stock behind the gun.
Further, that the body is balanced so that recoil is
taken by the whole frame. In tall pheasant
shooting, you should present the actual physical
appearance of stretching to stroke your bird out
of the sky

A back view of the moment of firing at a high
pheasant on the left. The inset reveals the problem
of guessing the height of tall pheasants. The three
posts are erected 10yd distant from each other.
The first or lowest board is 1yd in length, the
second or middle one 2yd in length, the third 3yd.
To the eye they all look alike

Dry Practice: Rabbit or Hare Shooting: 'Fire'
A rabbit breaks out on the right. The shooter, in the ready position, leans forward on his right leg to decline his body for the shoot

As you take fur on the right, your whole body should cant forward to take the shot from a natural position as the gun swings

A rabbit on the left. The body sways forward and the weight is taken on the left leg as the gun lifts from the ready position

'Fire' at a rabbit on the left. Compare this forward position for taking a ground shot with the stance assumed for high pheasants

A Norfolk farmer's shoot

(*Above*) Farmers shooting in 1943   (*Below*) Off to the shoot

have entered into a sweepstake in which we agreed that, at long range, we would try to kill before the others could. I usually lost. I have also been a member of a shoot in which every head of vermin, things like magpies, jays and grey squirrels which were shot, called for a reward of one pound from every gun in the line. It could be expensive if the luck of the day was not with you. Our host liked it because, while we were concentrating on lesser creatures within the law, he was saving his pheasants for another day.

The casual mood, the most enjoyable in the field, is what matters. Everyone shoots so much better when he is not trying to show off. A miss is not important. That is why I am out of sympathy with those Victorian and Edwardian gunners who shot for records.

In the field it is requisite above all else to have a basic knowledge of natural history. You ought to know, you will be unpopular if you don't, the quarry that is fair game, and what isn't. The ideal shot picks out, well in front of him, the two leaders in a covey of partridges. They are almost certainly the old birds. If they are killed the covey will break up and spread to improve the breeding stock on the manor. The ideal shot never raises his gun to a low, probably immature, pheasant. He will fly much better next time. The ideal gun never shoots fur in front but, holding the barrels of his gun flat against his shoulder, waits until the rabbit or the hare has passed before taking him behind.

In practice few of us, in the fervour of the chase, can pretend that we have not offended. I have an amusing recollection of a beautiful young woman, armed with a 20-bore, who in a partridge drive shot a squeaker pheasant. Her husband reprimanded her, only later himself to be found guilty of killing a carrier pigeon. On another shoot we had as a guest a member of a minor European royal family. Using a heavily-gilded over-and-under gun he began the day by bringing down a green woodpecker, and ended it by knocking off a brace of tame white doves. He was a good shot but since his experience in the field was mostly in the swamps of Turkey, he lacked discrimination. It is far better to know what you are firing at. Indeed it is always better, if you are unsure of the identification of a species, not to shoot at all. It is difficult enough to organise yourself to shoot legitimate game.

I recall a time when I had the best opportunity I have ever had of taking a right-and-left at woodcock. Two 'cock slipped silently out of the woods at an easy height straight to my own gun. At that time the Bols gin people in Holland offered a free bottle to anybody who could authenticate a genuine right-and-left. I had time to shout to my neighbours, 'Here comes a bottle of Bols gin.' I missed hopelessly with both barrels. I missed because I was thinking of the prize rather than keeping my mind on shooting correctly.

It is an interesting experiment to cast an eye at a neighbouring gun as birds come over him. It can also be done in a more leisurely way in the shooting school. Resist the natural inclination to look at the target. Just watch the rhythm of gun-mounting and footwork. Try and guess from the movement whether he has made a kill or a miss.

The man on his day never seems to be in a hurry. The sway of the balance of his body is at one with the lift of the gun to his shoulder. He mounts his gun unhurriedly, never hesitates as the butt bedding into his shoulder tightens the pressure of his trigger finger. He is balanced like a ballet dancer. When he breaks his gun, and a wisp of smoke eddies out of the chambers, you won't need to take a second look to know that he has killed clean.

By contrast, study the shot who is out of form, or perhaps never found it. He is at first hesitant, and then treats the gun in his hand with violent energy, dragging the trigger in his

Concentration, co-ordination

uncertainty the fallible fraction of a second after mounting. You will probably notice that he staggers a little on recoil. Look behind him and you need not doubt that another pheasant will live to cluck 'cock-up' on another day.

It is easy to say that the art of the sport—I am talking of driven birds when you are at a stand in the field—is to relax. It is very difficult on a big occasion, especially among strangers, to remain entirely calm. You cannot tell a covey of partridges, a flurry of pheasants, or a wayward woodcock, that you are not quite ready. You must be alert for a surprise at every second you stand at a numbered stick in the line of guns. Birds often break before the drive is supposed to have started.

I can only suggest that you try to adopt the attitude which marks the most proficient shots· When they move to their number their first action is to stamp out a safe platform for their feet. It may well be a ploughed field or a tussocky pasture. Next, they assess the distance to the line of the trees on the edge of the covert or, in partridge shooting especially, how they are placed behind the covering hedge.

The habit of measuring distances by eye is a valuable one. Most of us instinctively know the length of a cricket pitch. A 25yd range is equally familiar to a small-bore rifleman. It is useful to remember that the average tree in a covert in Britain is seldom much higher than 40 or 50ft. Your gun has a killing range of 40–60yd. A tall bird (I exclude wildfowl which are shot under completely different conditions) if he comes into your arc of fire, is almost never out of range of your gun. There is seldom an occasion, excluding an occasional wood pigeon, for a wild shot. If you shoot wildly, or if you delude yourself that a bird is beyond your compass, you will certainly miss. If you contain yourself and remember your gun drill, I hope that you will be surprised how often you can pull down a tall bird which somebody else thought was out of range.

(*Opposite*)
The evolution of the muzzleloader
(*Left to right*) A single-barrelled flint gun made by Henry Nock (1772–1804) incorporating his patent breeching in which the charge was ignited not from the side of the barrels, as hitherto, but from the centre.

A single-barrelled 12-bore by Joseph Manton (1795–1835) converted from flint to the percussion system.

A 12-bore double-barrelled percussion gun by John Manton (1780–1834), Joseph's brother.

The first successful hammerless breech-loading gun patented in 1872 by Theophilus Murcott at 68 Haymarket, London. Better known as 'Murcott's mouse trap' due to the sound that the action makes when it is cocked. Engraved on the barrel it is recorded that it was 'bound to shoot close' by W. W. Greener

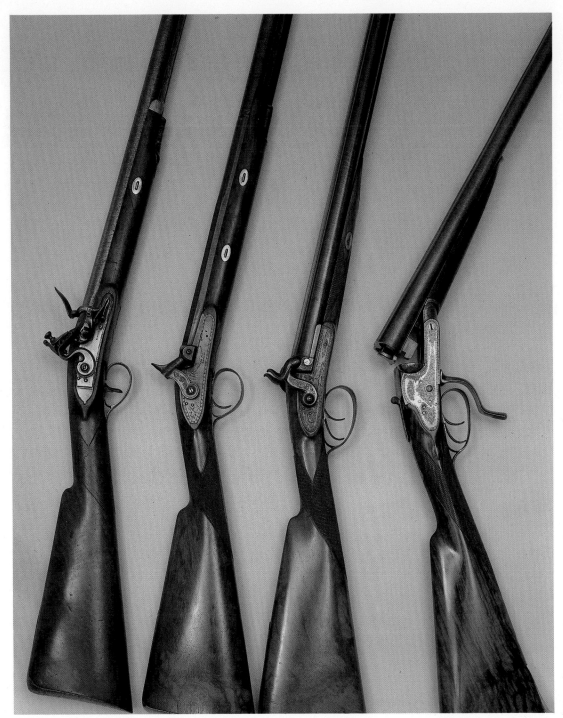

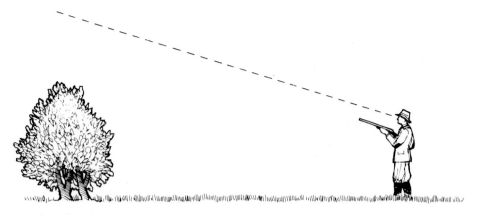

Partridge Shooting

In driven partridge shooting a whistle is normally sounded when birds are coming over. For good shooting it is fatal for the gun to allow himself to be distracted by anything which is happening down the line. His eyes should be fixed over the cover, 'into the blue', in front of him. A covey of partridges is not the fastest of birds. But they arrive so unexpectedly that constant attention, concentrated on the air ahead, is essential for good performance. That way you can kill, as you should, cleanly and well in front.

I have known specialist shots at tall pheasants who disdained to stand in the front line with other guns. They prefered to keep well back to deal with the high-flying cocks who had beaten the rest. They were all blessed with the perfect footwork, balance, and vertical lift to stop a pheasant when he looked as small as a partridge in the sky. But they were always well within range. The experts know it. It is only if you don't believe it possible that you shoot without conviction, and miss.

One of the most useful lessons in driven game shooting is that you must take your eye off the ground, and, waiting for birds to come over, 'stare into the blue'. Myself I am too

(Opposite)
In 1968 one of the master London gunmakers, Messrs Holland & Holland, built a matched set of five guns, the first of their kind ever made in 12-, 16-, 20-, 28-, and .410-bore. At the same time another set of five guns were started which were to be a pair of 12-, a pair of 20-, and a single 28-bore

curious ever to have followed the advice. I love watching too much what the guns in the other butts and stands are up to. But I follow the reasoning. If your eyes are not wandering about the landscape, if you are holding your gun in the 'ready' position, with a slight lift in preparation for action, the birds themselves will lift into your vision. You will gain a valuable second of time in gun-mounting.

You will notice in the field that some guns have a style which is other than the method I have recommended. King George V, an excellent shot, was an exponent of this school. When he mounted his gun he ran his left arm to full stretch up the barrels. Throughout his life he used hammer guns. Handling his weapons I was surprised to find that he also dismissed a half-cock in the actions. He believed that it was safer to carry a gun with hammers down, and quicker to shoot from full cock. None may argue with his idiosyncratic taste. There is no fault in it as a classical style. But he benefited from skilled loaders.

In the end, it is all a matter of what suits your personal performance. The King was shooting in the heyday of vast bags. So many birds were in the air to his gun that he could pick and choose. He favoured the birds which came at a level angle of 45°. His style was a deadly method of dealing with them. He dropped birds, as I have seen other first class shots achieve later, in a small circle. George VI, his son, may well have been the better shot. He could handle all the improbable chances offered by wildfowl when he was in a hide in a barrel on the Norfolk marshes.

It is normally unusual to shoot with a pair of guns today, never mind the matched three which were cultivated in the extravagance of Victorian and Edwardian shooting parties when guns travelled with an army of attendants. There are still occasions in the coverts and on the moors when a pair of guns, and a loader, are the order of the shoot. It is an arrangement which should not be attempted casually. To be effective and safe the loader should be as well-trained as the gun. The classic anecdote tells how, after the gun had shot, he threw his weapon to the ground. In proper practice, after firing the shooter should push the small of the butt in his right hand to the loader and collect the second gun by the fore-end with his left. The loader should be half-doubled up to leave a full field of fire for the following shots. There is an art in it in which the loader's skill is not much less than that of the man handling the guns. A first-class loader, as I have reason to know, can increase the performance of his gun by at least ten per cent.

Performance, the average of cartridges fired to kills, is normally exaggerated. I fancy that even top shots have flattered themselves with the totals they have claimed in the bag. My own guess is that a very good shot might kill once out of four cartridges expended. I very much doubt whether Lord Walsingham or the Marquis of Ripon, never mind the vast bags they recorded in their game books, put up a better show over the years than four-to-one. You and I are lucky if we kill twenty per cent of the game fired at. We are all a little inclined to tell white lies to ourselves. Shotgun shooting is not that easy.

I have written largely about driven gameshooting. It is the most testing form of the sport. It is nevertheless true that most shotgun shooting is what is called rough shooting. Without the organisation provided by keepers and beaters, stops and flankers and numbered drives, walking up, usually in company with a party of disorderly dogs, is the order of the day.

I am disinclined to dismiss it. Some of the best sporting days in my life have been spent rough shooting. We never achieved the sort of bags that are collected in a driven shoot,

The Gamekeeper

(*Above*) The Beaters

(*Below*) Partridges and pheasants

Expectation

Shooting lady, suitably attired

(*Above*) A fine bag

(*Below*) Patiently waiting, dogs and man

The good days—1943

although we made up for it in the collection of 'various'. Many of the good fellows who joined us, in different financial circumstances, might have been top shots themselves in the big days in the coverts. But we had inordinate fun.

The charm of the rough shoot is that it extends gun know-how to another dimension. In driven shooting, a team presents the birds to you. The dog-handlers organise the pick-up. Driven birds are taller and more difficult than those you walk up for yourself. But, indeed, rough shooting, until the middle of the nineteenth century, was everybody's sport. You work your own dogs as springers of game rather than retrievers. The tactics of the shoot are all your own. And you have to carry your own bag of game home.

I have learnt more about natural history when I have been carrying a gun on my own, with a good dog ranging in front of me, than I ever have on a driven game shoot. Reading dogs, for example, is a recreation in itself.

I had a spaniel for many years whose habits I got to know so well that I could assess from his nose and foot movements what he was marking. I knew when he was on to a pheasant or a woodcock. He had a tricky backward behaviour in an area infested with adders in which I was shooting. At some point in his life I had reason to believe that he had been bitten by one. He was ill at the time but, although I was then ignorant of the cause, he survived. Ever after, he gave me fair warning when an adder was coiled up, usually at the head of a rabbit burrow. Occasionally he misled me.

I recollect times when he gave a clear mark that he had found a woodcock, and nothing broke out of the patch of cover. I cursed him until an old countryman told me that, if you look carefully when that happens, you will see a jenny wren. Wrens have a game scent, he said. He was right.

The lessons of shooting alone are invaluable. It is not even true that all the targets are easy. I have pulled off showy shots at pheasant in a gap in the trees in thick woodland. I have been surprised to kill a bird in a snap shot in a 10ft gap between the trees. It proves the tremendous importance in straight shotgun shooting of eye and gun coming together when there is no time to think what you are doing. Good shooting, if your gun-mounting is balanced, is instinctive.

It is not so easy for a walking gun to achieve good gun-mounting as it is for one at a fixed stand. It is not so easy for a man crouched in a pigeon hide in the harvest field to make a rhythmic swing of the gun. A wildfowler, on a cold winter's dawn in a hole in the ground, has his own problems although he may be happier with a shorter-stocked gun. But the rules, in all circumstances, are the same.

If you are not in the standing position you must use your gun from the waist and shoulders. It is not so comfortable as it is when you can run recoil into your boots. But if you do not hesitate on your trigger-pressing at the moment your shoulder comes in to meet the butt it is unlikely that you will notice recoil at all. I recollect an occasion in Africa when, in the search for a dinner, I picked up in haste a .404 magnum Express rifle in the mistaken belief that it was a miniature .22 rifle. I never noticed the recoil until I thought about it later; indeed, until the meat was in the pot. If you are well-balanced in the field you will not notice the recoil either.

It is undeniable that the 12-bore shotgun in inexperienced hands can split lips and black eyes. It is the sweetest weapon in hands which have been trained to use it correctly. Throw the shoulder and bodyweight into it and you will not suffer much even after a thousand rounds.

'*There are four different kinds of clay target shooting. Three of them are specifically for the sport of competitive clay pigeon shooting, and the fourth is designed to simulate the conditions of shooting various kinds of game on the field. Down-the-line, Skeet and Trap shooting are sports in their own rights, with a complete range of competitions.*'

MICHAEL ROSE
(Chief Instructor at West London Shooting Grounds)

CHAPTER 15

COMPETITION SHOOTING

Competition shotgun practice, in many respects the antithesis of game gun shooting in the field, dates from the last third of the reign of Queen Victoria. The social barriers of the time, never mind the financial ones, precluded the vast majority of people from shooting in the pheasant coverts and on the grouse moors and partridge manors of the landed gentry. But the popularity of shooting at moving targets was increasing with every year of the century. The sport that developed was shooting live pigeons or, more modestly, sparrows released from trap-doors set in the ground.

After all this time it is easy to adopt an attitude of disgust to the trap-shooting of captive birds. It still goes on in most of the Latin countries. It was only stopped in Monte Carlo at the instigation of Princess Grace. It continued in Britain until the early twenties. It might have survived longer but for a campaign for its abolition in the *Daily Express*, arising out of an incident in which a competitor at a shooting match at Dover dropped a dead bird on to a coffin as it was being lowered into a grave in an adjoining cemetry. Earlier public feeling had been shocked when, in a similar incident, a pigeon flopped into the lap of Queen Alexandra at Hurlingham, splashing her with its blood. Yet when a Bill was introduced to make an end to it under the Captive Birds Act of 1922 a million-and-a-quarter signatures were collected in a petition to keep it going.

For many people at the time it no more occurred that pigeon-shooting from traps was cruel than it seemed cruel to the ironworkers of Staffordshire to put terriers to maim a tethered bull, or to Good Queen Bess to hold a bear-bait. True, the shooting of pigeons or sparrows from traps was not regarded as a gentleman's recreation. It attracted much the same crowd, people of much the same class, as dog-racing and professional boxing today.

Robert Churchill told me that one of his earliest recollections was riding in the pony trap with the customers' guns and cartridges to the Gun Clubs at Notting Hill and Hurlingham during the summer, and the Welsh Harp at Hendon in winter, for the matches. They

attracted as many gamblers as shooters. For that reason the matches were usually arranged on Mondays when there was little horse-racing going on.

The ground was drawn in the shape of a half-circle, with five traps running along the diameter. The distance from the traps to the half-circular barrier around the perimeter was 16yd. The shooter stood back between 20 and 40yd, according to the terms of the match, from the traps. The live birds, one at a time, were released by pulling a lever. To record a 'kill', the shooter had to drop his bird within the barrier. Outside it 'killers' were posted to knock the wounded on the head.

The pigeons employed were known as Lincoln Blue Rocks, small and very fast. Their tails were trimmed, not to impede their flight, as is often supposed, but to get rid of fouled feathers so that they flew more strongly. It is a fragment of history that the pigeons which now infest almost the whole of central London are largely descendants of the Lincoln Blue Rocks who defeated the guns when they burst out of the traps.

The winner of a live pigeon match was the shooter who could make the longest succession of clean kills. Gunmakers and publicans put up the prizes, sometimes as much as 250 sovereigns, supplied the pigeons, and financed the organisation of the shoot. Entry for the competitors was on the basis of a sovereign a bird and the shooters went on investing until, one by one, they fell out of the running. The entry fees went into the pocket of the man who had staked the match.

Irrespective of humanitarian considerations, it was a rogue's game because the gamblers could so easily, and so often did, bribe the favourite to withdraw in the interests of a dark horse. But there was big money in it for the professionals. Less than ten years after he had founded his own business in London, and his nephew Robert Churchill had joined him, E. J. Churchill recorded proudly in his gun catalogue that pigeon shooters competing with his guns had netted £4,283 3s 4d that season in stake money. It was a thousand pounds more than any other London gunmaker could claim. And it was not just pounds, but golden sovereigns.

The eventual abolition of the shooting of live birds made way for the spring trap. With increasing ingenuity ways were devised to throw clay discs, at any angle and at any height,

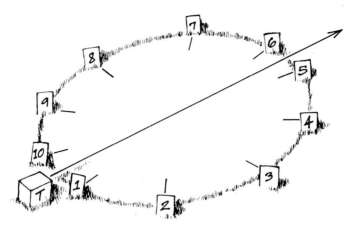

The most simple layout for a shooting ground

Primitive traps, or spring throwers designed to eject either clays or hollow glass balls stuffed with feathers, were introduced during the eighties of the last century, when shooting out of traps at live birds was beginning to fall into disrepute. Live pigeon shooting, in the first quarter of the present century, was made illegal in Britain. Modern trap-shooting and the automatic clay target have introduced a new and humane competitive sport. The diagram indicates how, with a single trap and a 30yd oval pegged out with numbers, the shooter can practise with a complete variety of shots from angled stands

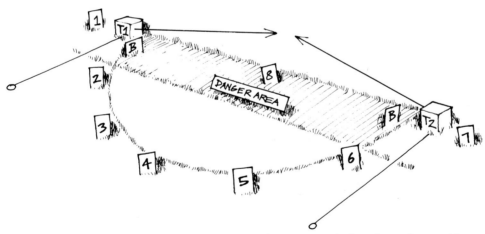

The layout of a double skeet stand, developed in North America, is the best form of competitive clay pigeon shooting for the average game shot. It has all the charm, from different stands, of clock golf. The basis of the method of shooting in this way is that the guns 'point out their targets'; that is, they hold their guns ahead of them in almost the position they intend breaking their birds and, with barely perceptible movement, yet perfect timing, make a snap. There is an art in shooting from each stand in the clock-shaped course as the double clays are thrown over. It can defeat men who are top game shots in the field. Game in the field defeats the best skeet shots.

to test the skill of the gunner. In the first shooting schools in this century the notion was that it would be a preparation for shooting in the field. It is a valuable introduction.

With the passage of the years, clay pigeon shooting has developed into a game in its own right. It has its styles which are not necessarily the most suitable ones in the sport of game gun shooting and, indeed, it has its own fashions in weapons; but it has become a significant factor, and a financially important one, in shotgun shooting in our time.

The competitive game largely owes its development to America and the continent. Notably its exponents largely favour the North American peaked cap and the badged shooting coat which have never been quite accepted in the English and Scottish game scene. They have also adopted, almost universally, the over-and-under, repeating, or automatic arm. Pistol grip stocks and single triggers are favoured. The weapons are ideal for the game which has evolved.

They are heavier than the guns which are normally in use in the field. But, because they are heavier the recoil is gentler. The over-and-unders are slower to load than side-by-side barrels, but in competition it does not matter. In clay-pigeon competition shooting, swing does not enter into the game as it does when you are trying to pick out a brace from a covey of partridges. Clay pigeon shots look for a point, and carry their guns to meet it. Most of them mount their guns for the pull with a muscular balance not under the squeeze of their arm but with the butt vibrating just short of the bed of their shoulders, as they used to when pigeons were not clay discs but live birds. The target when it appears, unlike live game in wild conditions, does not change course. The experts snap it, without much body movement, as it rises in the air.

The tableaux for competitive clay-shooting so far devised are three. They are, respectively, down-the-line—the simplest form of away-shooting; trap—clay discs sprung from a trench; and skeet—the clock-golf game named after the Norwegian word for 'shoot' which is widely practised in the USA. They are all specialised competitive games. It is proper to add that a proficient game shot can be made to look a clown when he has to call 'pull' and 'mask' on a skeet layout. Alternatively, a first-class clay pigeon shot is liable to be very unhappy in a driven game shoot. I cannot emphasise enough the difference in the required skills for good shooting in both.

'In the normal equipment of a well-made flint gun of the early nineteenth century, there were of course many additional fittings—some of a practical, and others of a more or less fantastic nature—which a shooter could indulge in if he were of the temperament that delights in a multiplicity of small tools. There was practically no end to the variety of worms and jags, cleaning brushes, oil bottles, powder and shot measures, and patented "combination" tools which he could acquire if the mania seized him, or if he should be so rash as to entrust a really enterprising gunmaker with an open order for a guncase, to be fitted "regardless of expense" with every shooting requisite that the tradesman's ingenuity might suggest.'

J. N. GEORGE
(*English Guns and Rifles*)

CHAPTER 16

THE ORNAMENTS OF THE GUN

An elegant shotgun, like a handsome woman, is incomplete without its beauty accessories. The top gunmakers have traditionally presented a matched pair like a bridal couple in an oak-lined, brass-cornered, leather-covered case bedded in green or red baize, and embossed with its owner's initials or a coronet for nobility.

In a complete trousseau you will find ramrods, square oil bottles, silvered snap-caps, mops and wire brushes, and a turnscrew for removing the locks. In a case of second-hand guns it is surprising how often the turnscrew is missing. The reason is that the finely-tempered tool is so often borrowed for other work and never returned. Anyhow, it ought never to have been introduced into the guncase in the first place. Only a shooting man with a craftsman's skill in his hands can be trusted to remove the locks of a breechloader without burring the slits in the pins. The wise sportsman leaves that sort of work to the professional.

In truth the equipment which gunmakers supply with their weapons is on the whole useless to the average shooter. It all looks ornamental in the case. It is best to leave it there, and cosset your guns in a more practical if not more pedestrian fashion. The sportsman should not be seduced, although he often is, by the exquisite gadgets which the gunmakers are eager to supply.

It is questionable whether the elaborate double guncase of the past is other than an inconvenience. It is confoundedly heavy to hump about in a world without servants. It fits uncomfortably into the boot of a car. A compact double guncase is much more in keeping with our times. It does not look as luxurious as one of those oversized jewel cases of the past, but it is easier to live with.

The care of guns, much simpler now than before the coming of non-corrosive ammunition, is a matter best handled without the accoutrements which the gunmakers still provide. The squat oil bottles, pretty as they are, are left-overs. What is needed today is an aerosol spray to give a light oil touch to the working parts.

Theoretically, with modern cartridges, your gun will be free of fouling. In practice it would be inadvisable not to clean it as carefully as you needed to in the old days when a dirty gun rotted the metal of the barrels. Damp is still an enemy. On salty coastlines it is a formidable one.

The law of the gunroom has not changed. Ideally, the gunner ought to have a rack of rods fitted with oily mops, wire brushes, and card-headed ones to clean the barrels. An aerosol, filled with Young's excellent cleaner, is ideal to give a light squirt under the blades of the triggers and down the gutters on both sides of the ribs where rust can be insidious.

The stock should be nourished and polished lovingly to bring out the figure of the walnut. It is worth knowing that if you make a dent in the stock—it usually happens when you bash it against the brass buckles of your cartridge bag—the gunmaker can sweat it out. If you dent the barrels, as so often happens, it is a matter of major importance to take the gun to the maker to relieve the damage. Otherwise, every shot you fire will wound the metal until, ultimately, it fails.

Make sure that you learn, as a woman does, that there is no short cut to beauty treatment. Guns must be thoroughly cleaned. It is no use rubbing the brush and the mop in the first fifteen inches of the barrels only. You must see it through. When you think that the barrels are clean, study them through the muzzle end until you find that they are free of streaks and shine moon-bright to your eye. The cosmetics of your gun are not the least of its charms.

The ornaments, like the clothes of the shooters, have changed with the wayward fashions of the years. A guest at a shooting party in Victorian and Edwardian times arrived with a formidable quantity of gear. Not least among the gear were his cartridge magazines. They became objects of social importance. A sportsman carried what he expected to shoot.

Now outdated, magazines, normally partitioned to carry two hundred or five hundred cartridges, still have a collector's interest. They are beautiful pieces of cabinet-making, oak-

(*Opposite*)
The development of the breechloader
(*Left to right*) A double-barrelled top lever 10-bore built by J. P. Caldbrough and Bros of London (1893–1895) for wildfowlers, the barrels defined as 'fine Damascus'.

A double-barrelled push lever 12-bore by John Blanch & Son of Gracechurch Street, London (1809–1819).

A double-barrelled underlever 12-bore by W. W. Greener, London & Birmingham (1878–1965). Defined on the barrels as 'laminated steel'.

A 14-bore double-barrelled pinfire arm by W. Gallyon, 66 Bridge Street, Cambridge (1784 to date). A brief development between percussion weapons and central firing cartridges.

A double-barrelled contemporary easy-opening hammerless ejector by E. J. Churchill Ltd, London (1892 to 1981)

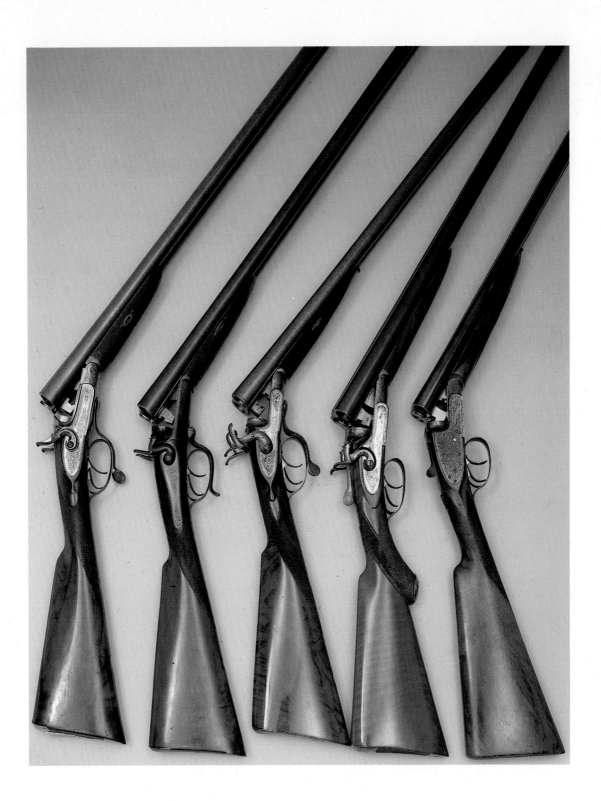

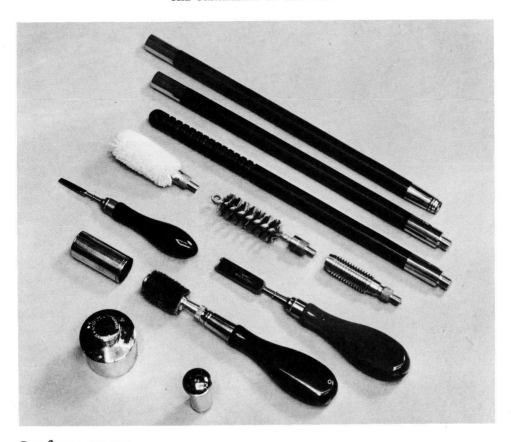

Gear from a gun case
Turnscrew, oil bottle, snap-caps, mops and ram rod—the gear that is part of the ornamentation of guncases

framed and embellished in leather of the blonde London finish. They were horse-drawn from stand to stand on shooting days in the ammunition cart. Even when cartridges were twopence each they were kept locked with a brass key until it was necessary to refill the cartridge bags.

Surprisingly, nobody has really improved on the type of pigskin cartridge bag designed by the inventive Payne-Gallwey at the turn of the century. With a metal rim to hold it in position with the flap back, it is still the most widely used in the field. Cartridge belts and bandoliers of various degrees of efficiency and ingenuity have come into use, but there are objections to all of them, chiefly because the smooth rhythm of gun mounting is disturbed by a weight round the midriff or across the shoulder. Without a loader, or when shooting alone, the best place to store cartridges is in the side pockets of your jacket.

I have never traced the evolution of the shooting stick, but it has a venerable history undoubtedly dating from the time when driven game shooting began. Before that nobody could sit down when they were walking up. The first shooting sticks, with seats like cane

Norfolk liars—game counters were used in the nineteenth century by individual guns to keep the score of fur and feather killed. Nobody bothers with them anymore

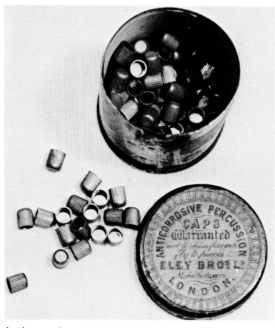

Anti-corrosive percussion caps

chairs, were probably the inspiration of a portly or elderly sportsman who was a bit weak in his pins. Today it is an accessory of all driven game shots, eschewed only by energetic young men who are probably sent off to walk with the beaters. Incidentally the metal of shooting sticks is one of the commonest causes of dents in barrels when they are carried together with the gun.

No doubt the increasing use of gun sleeves, not merely canvas slips but sheepskin-lined covers with a zip and shoulder strap, is one of the most protective ways of looking after a gun. Aboard a tractor-driven trailer lined with straw bales for seats, the usual passenger service on shoots between one stand and another, the gun is cushioned in a fleece lining. In the boot of the car it is less likely to take a knock. Among the ornaments of the gun the gun sleeve is a practical one.

The gadgets of the shotgun, which proliferated so wildly in muzzleloading days, have become increasingly unnecessary. It used to be said that no man should go into the field without a cartridge extractor in his pocket to pull out recalcitrant paper cases from the breech. Nowadays you are unlikely to need one once in a thousand rounds. If the stock of your gun is too short or if your gun handling is untidy, you can ameliorate the problem by slipping a removable rubber pad over the butt. If you are bruising your trigger finger as you fire, due to bad gun-mounting, you can have a rubber ring fitted to your guard. If you suffer from 'gun-headache' you can bite a bit of indiarubber between your teeth. If you are wildly off target, it may help for a time to get 'a blind eye' from Messrs Cogswell and Harrison to bring the gun into line from a one-eyed stance. Far better to go back to the shooting school to find out what you are so obviously doing wrong.

All sportsmen equip themselves with the tackle of their pastimes. The worst offenders are unquestionably anglers. When an angler dies he generally leaves behind him more gear in the way of flies, boxes, floats, rods and reels than he ever used in actual practice in his life. The eager shooter is just as likely to litter his house with the paraphernalia of the gunroom. It is coincidental that shooters are often anglers too. I fear that I must count myself among the sinners.

Yet the gunroom, properly organised, can be among the most pleasant places in a country house. It is important to have a rack of cleaning rods, each one with its own mop and brush, set up like cues in a billiards room. The various cleaning oils should be set up on their own shelf. There should be a drawer for chamber brushes, old tooth brushes (ideal for cleaning mud out of the checkering on the stocks), oily rags, clean rags, a skin of chamois and wax polish for the walnut. Do not overdo it. There is nothing that a shotgun likes less than over-oiling. To be clean, yes, but you can gum up the works if you overdo the oil.

One of the most useful accessories, if you have the space and a firm work bench, is a miniature vice which is ideal for gripping gun barrels when you are cleaning. Remember to put a piece of leather between the jaws to prevent bruising of the barrels. Messrs Parker Hale of Birmingham, although largely rifle specialists, also supply some of the most useful cleaning and working equipment for the shotgun.

The last, probably the least, of the appurtenances attached to the gun is *The Game Book*. I remember that I was presented with one on my twenty-first birthday, a luxurious volume in hand-tooled leather spaced out for the record of the feather and fur I had brought to my gun. There were spaces for grouse, partridges and pheasants, wildfowl, hares and rabbits and deer. For a year or more when my total bag might account for a pigeon or two, a few rabbits in the harvest fields, an occasional wild duck and, unusually, a partridge or a pheasant, I kept the record religiously. I even glued in a feather of my more colourful kills.

It is absurd that when the time came to share in big days in the field I lost all interest in the book. The biggest bag I ever recorded was three partridges. I have now lost *The Game Book*. I believe that shooting men, like myself, have now largely lost their interest in collecting records. It is fun to look at the old game books, but nowadays the sport is enough.

'Jean, nankeen, fustian, velveteen, and all the other articles that formed the sporting wardrobe of our fathers are now completely "snuffed out" by the admirable Scotch woollen fabrics, which may be had of every hue and texture, and are thus suited to every variety of climate and temperature. A complete suit of the same stuff for general shooting is the most advisable, and saves an increase of baggage in travelling'.

LT-COL PETER HAWKER
(in the year before his death in 1853)

The
Burberry.

CHAPTER 17

THE CLOTHES FOR THE GUN

The right dress for shotgun work has taken longer to develop than the evolution of the gun itself. Although it is always dangerous to bet on fashionable trends I venture to think that it is only in recent years that the coming of huskies and loose shooting coats of various sorts has approached a solution. Not a final solution because the artificial yarn is rather too slippery for sweet gun-mounting. The problem can partly be resolved with leather patches on the shoulders. The objection to the new types of shooting coat is that, in the field, even in contemporary estimation, they do not look right.

In big shoots in England and Scotland nothing has changed very much since Colonel

Peter Hawker recommended home-spun woollen tweeds. You would scarcely be welcome if you appeared on a top shoot with a peaked cap and a showy nylon shooting coat. The style which the Americans adopt is certainly more sensible but it is not generally accepted.

By tradition, tweeds are still the rule. The well-dressed man at a shoot appears in a heather or russet colour which is unlikely to distract the birds. His purpose is to blend into the landscape. The Highland tweeds, products of the sheep, are the perfect natural colours.

The tailoring has always been in debate. The Norfolk men thought they had it right—they still think so—when they introduced a tweed jacket with gussets between the shoulders at the back. It allowed for a smoother gun swing without sacrifice of cut. The Norfolk belted jacket, with a generosity of pockets, worn with knickerbockers, boots and calf-length spats, was a style which emerged at the beginning of this century. It is respected, with minor modifications, in all formal shoots today.

Autumnal colours are still the rule. Leather patches on the shoulders and elbows, as Colonel Hawker recommended, are an indication of experience. Gumboots are now some-times worn in dirty weather, but, for balance, pernickerty shots prefer well-oiled and studded boots or brogues. Spats, the sort worn by King Edward VII and George V are no longer in fashion, yet they were useful in their way. They kept the legs free of harvest-bugs, burrs, straw and bramble waste.

Robert Churchill suggested that a shooting jacket should be cut in the 'raglan' style of an overcoat, very loose under the armpits, and far more free than the Norfolk jacket. In his definition of the best clothes for shooting practice he was undoubtedly right. But the 'raglan cut', comfortable though it is, is not decorative on human shoulders. I fancy that is the reason why it has not been widely adopted.

There is no doubt that wildfowlers are leading the way to new styles in shotgun fashions. Without being constricted by uncomfortable conventions they are dressing themselves to suit the vagaries of wind and weather. I am sure that in due course fashion in the clothes for the gun will follow them. It has remained the same for too long.

I doubt whether the proper attire for the shooting field has been anything other than an affectation. Certainly the old gunners in muzzleloading days wore all the wrong clothes. In their heavy cloth they were always at a disadvantage. In our own times the right dress for a big shoot is still open to question.

On rough shooting days I have always been amused to notice the different kinds of apparel which sportsmen assume. I have come to the conclusion that nobody has really decided yet what the best clothes are for a day's shooting. I have had guests in jodpurs and gumboots, corduroys and windcheaters, and, on one occasion, a girl with a 20-bore who struggled through a ploughed field in high-heeled shoes. I recollect that, among the eccentrics in the field, there was one in Victorian times who had a hat made out of a hedgehog.

It is disciplinary to remember that, in the field, a hat of some kind or another is essential when shooting partridges, grouse or wildfowl. A bare forehead is enough to turn them. For those, like myself, who do not like wearing a hat, it is true to say that, once pheasants have settled in their course, they are not diverted in their flight at the sight of a bare head. But, whatever your personal prejudices, and mine, it is still wiser to have a cover over your forehead. In pigeon-shooting it is essential. A mask over the lower part of your head is desirable too.

King George V by Spy from the original at Sandringham

It is a small point, but even today, when guests are invited to lunch in a shooting lodge or even the house, it is precautionary to put on a pair of slippers on coming inside. You can never get all the mud off with a scraper. It is also restful for the feet to have a change out of sweaty boots.

In cold weather it is a blessing to have a pair of shooting mitts to keep you warm round the wrists and the back of your hands and, at the same time, leave your trigger finger free. Full gloves are definitely dangerous and are also a barrier to accurate shooting practice. You cannot expect to have the delicate touch on the triggers if your directing finger is clothed in leather or even wool. Neither, if you are loading yourself, can you expect to handle your cartridges with smooth expediency.

It is arguable that for shooting you should wear a belt rather than braces so that you have the fullest freedom of movement in your shoulders and no restriction at your waist. If you wear braces, make sure that the buckle is well out of the way of the pit of your shoulder where you sink the gun butt. If you have to pile on woollies against the weather you are essentially lengthening the stock. You can do something about it by shortening your grip on the gun. But extra layers of clothes unquestionably put the shooter at a disadvantage. Wildfowlers, who with good reason are prone to overpad themselves, should use guns shorter in the stock than they would in the field when 'warm September brings the fruit, and sportsmen then begin to shoot'.

The tweeds of today are softer, lighter and much better woven than they used to be. They are also far more expensive, but so is the sport of shooting. It is worth spending as much as you can afford on the clothes for the gun, as on the gun itself. Shooting is an athletic exercise. You will never be any good if you do not think about your wardrobe as consciously as any other sportsman. I am afraid that too many people who go shooting, and make a mess of it, labour under the delusion that it is not an art, demanding constant practice and even sartorial attention, but a sport in which every proper man should naturally excel. If you hope to touch a feather, it is admonitory, if not the first consideration, to look to your own feathers in the field.

'Learning from books is obviously a more difficult way of learning than by taking lessons at a shooting school. But it can be done. I taught myself to use a fly-rod that way.'

M.H.

CHAPTER 18

A GUNROOM BOOKSHELF

The short list which follows is intended only as a foundation to which a sportsman can add at his own discretion. I myself can think of many good books which I might have included here; but the way to begin is to assemble the skeleton of the subject. The bare bones of the literature of the shotgun, up till now, seem to me to wire together something like this:

Instructions to Young Sportsmen, in all that relates to guns and shooting, by Colonel Peter Hawker

An antiquarian might argue that *The Boke of St Albans*, a manuscript of 1486 attributed to a mysterious figure named Dame Juliana Berners, is the English introduction to the pursuits of the chase. But, in her age, hunting meant falconry. Gervaise Markham, in the first quarter of the seventeenth century, made the earliest known reference to shooting as a method of bringing game to hand. But, to achieve it, he favoured nets and gins, the traditional methods of his times.

Colonel Hawker, as I have discussed in Chapter 3, was the Hampshire man who pioneered game-shooting as a gentleman's recreation. He, more than anyone, invented shooting as a field sport in the pregnant years when the shotgun was developed from the flintgun into the breechloader. He did not live to see the new baby but he certainly arranged the accouchement.

Nine editions of Hawker's book were published during his lifetime, the first in 1814 when he came back a wounded soldier from the Peninsular War. The tenth edition was revised posthumously by his son in 1857. From the first edition to the last, as the evolution of the shotgun caught up with him, Hawker enthusiastically revised his text.

Any collector who has all ten versions of Hawker's book in good condition on his shelves has a treasure. He was by no means a great writer. He is too anecdotal for that. But he was a true innovator and showed the way to the generation after him.

Indeed, he has much the same place in sporting literature as the Rev Gilbert White of Selborne has in his own natural history notes. White was no master of the written word.

He is immortal because in the eighteenth century he invented a new approach to the study of wild life. All who came after him, far better writers, have tramped in his footsteps. Hawker has the same claim on posterity.

The Modern Shooter, practical instructions and directions for every description of inland and coast shooting by Captain Lacy

I have seen a letter, in Colonel Hawker's own hand, in which he violently protested that Captain Lacy's book was a plagiarism of his own. Lacy, who published his own book in 1842, was clearly influenced by the success which already attended Hawker's work. But it was inevitable that others would come along, including myself, to write on the same subject.

Although in the fashion of the times he litters his book with literary tags (Hawker did not), as an author he shows a quite remarkable prescience of modern shooting practice. Educated at Repton, Lacy was a Cheshire man with his feet square on the grass. His literary style may be tiresome at times, but you can learn more from him about period shooting business than Hawker.

I prefer his work to other books of the period like *Oakleigh's Shooting Code* and *Wilson and Oakleigh's Rod and Gun*. *Pierce Egan's Book of Sports* gives a glimpse of the mood of the early part of the nineteenth century. But I would not include these three on a basic gunroom shelf.

The Gun and its Development by W. W. Greener

This is a classic. First published as a modest book in 1881 it became, in its ninth revised edition in 1910, a volume which is increasingly sought by bibliophiles and shooting men. I have not hesitated to use some of the woodcuts of gun actions in this book. I doubt if there is any craftsman today who can better these anonymous cuts.

W. W. Greener, the son of a gunmaker, was one of the Birmingham masters who challenged London, and even invaded it. Westley Richards was another. It is arguable whether the best of the London craftsmen, boastful as they were, could really do better than the men in small shops in the Midlands, who did not disdain the cheap market, but who also made guns which competed with the best-finished guns in the trade.

In 1940 during World War II, when Britain had her back against the wall, I recollect that an appeal was made to America for arms, any arms, to hold off an invasion. It fell to me to look over a heap of rubbish which well-wishers in the USA had sent over here for us to defend outselves with. Among the muzzleloaders, even flintlocks, I picked up a gun in a different class. On a gold plate on the butt, I read: 'To Annie Oakley, "Little Sure Shot" from W. W. Greener.' It was a gift from the great English gunmaker to the star of Buffalo Bill's Circus. I wonder what has happened to it now.

It is sad that so many of the great names in the English gunmaking trade have gone. There is no Greener any more, no Purdey, no Holland, no Lancaster, no Boss, no Churchill, no Manton. The tradition is preserved by other names. There are now very few of the craftsmen left whose names belong to the past. But so many of the others, like Greener's, survive in their books. That is why I so eagerly recommend you to create a shelf for them.

Peter Hawker's Diaries

Back to Hawker. At the turn of the nineteenth century, interest in Hawker grew. Payne-Gallwey got his hands on the manuscript of Hawker's diaries which the Colonel had kept

throughout his life. He published them in two volumes in 1892. Subsequently, Eric Parker, a distinguished writer on shotgun matters, and then editor of *The Field*, brought out a single edited volume in 1931 which I prefer.

He discovered, as so often happens in family papers, that much had been excised. Hawker married twice. The children of the first marriage resented the wife of the second. So Mrs Hawker the second scarcely appears in the diaries at all.

The books, castrated as they obviously are, are important in the description of the social scene of the period. I include both of them on my short list for the bookshelf.

Shooting by Lord Walsingham and Sir Ralph Payne-Gallwey, Bt. (Two volumes, Field and Covert, Moor and Marsh.)

The Badminton Library (1889) was perhaps the most important contribution to the new school of game gun shooting. The two volumes appeared under the names of Lord Walsingham and Sir Ralph Payne-Gallwey. Walsingham was one of the best shots of his time, but I have little doubt that Payne-Gallwey wrote most of the words. Walsingham had no distinction as a writer, however good he was in the field; and, ultimately, he went bankrupt.

I cannot recommend these two books, excellent though they were in their day, to the modern shooter. They are curiously defensive of the great shoots which were fashionable in their time. The attitude to wildfowling, with heavy-bored guns and punt guns, is out of date. The books fill a gap in the bookshelf because they represent an important part of the shotgun's place in English rural history.

High Pheasants in Theory and Practice by Ralph Payne-Gallwey

The essential lesson of this monograph is that Payne-Gallwey endeavoured to prove by practical experiment—he was a great experimentalist—that really tall pheasants, shot dead in the air, show no mark on their carcases of the shot which killed them. The notion is that the blast of the shot is sufficient to destroy the air pockets which support them on the wing. They are probably killed in their fall to the ground. It is still a theoretical matter.

A mere forty years ago antique arms, with rare exceptions, had no collectors' value. Gunmakers and dealers gave them away. Today they are commanding explosively rising prices. Established books on shooting history are also in high demand. I simply commend out of my own reading what I think will be regarded in the future as the classics:

The Lonsdale Library

Shooting by Moor, Field and Shore: Various Authors

I cannot recommend this book, although it has claims to the shelf. Designed under the title of the *Lonsdale Library* to succeed the *Badminton Library* of the nineteenth century, it has no pattern because it is an anthology written by a group of authors. I very much doubt whether anybody has read it from end to end, nor would wish to.

It belongs on the bookshelf because on the frontispiece it shows the Yellow Earl, Lord Lonsdale, shooting with three guns (1929).

A History of Firearms by H. B. C. Pollard

There is no question that this is the pioneer work of modern times. Hugh told me that, as a schoolboy at Westminster, he dragged his way to class, stopping at every gunshop he could find on the way. In his maturity, he produced the first serious study of firearms (1926)

Sir Ralph Payne-Gallwey in his gunroom at Thirkleby Hall, Thirsk, North Yorkshire, in 1913. The most inventive of the great shots of his times he exhibited a double-barrelled breechloading punt gun which was in advance of anything seen previously. He was the creator of Payne-Gallwey shooting bags, and the gaiters, shooting sticks, and gun-cleaning outfits that bear his name. Although he died in 1916, his books on shooting still ornament gunroom bookshelves

since W. W. Greener's *The Gun and its Development*. Pollard's was the more formidable book because, intellectually, he was the more formidable man. Nevertheless, he would have been the first to agree that his history of firearms has been updated by later students. There was a project, which failed, in which it was planned to establish the work, like a medical textbook, as standard. Unfortunately, the job fell into the hands of amateurs, knowledge-able ones, but people who did not know how to create a work of reference; or how to photograph weapons.

Pollard was a remarkable man. He shrank from the public gaze into country-house obscurity. He was a soldier and author who was also a criminologist, a microscopist, a photographer, a scientist with a 'useful knowledge' in his own words, 'of anatomy and chemistry'; and, above all, he knew more than any man in his time about firearms. Reserved and thin-lipped he was reluctant to talk to strangers. He said of himself that he liked things rather than people. I got on with him. I have no reservations about one whom I regard as one of the most remarkable men that I have known in my life.

His *History of Firearms*, and his other books, are a most valuable introduction to shooting. I particularly commend his now rare work *The Sportsman's Cookery Book*.

How to Shoot and Churchill's Game Shooting

In effect Pollard briefly rationalised in words Churchill's method of game-shooting. Recently I myself enlarged on it in a longer book. The work belongs on any gunroom bookshelf because it sets down the system of straight shooting which is now accepted. Although Churchill's teaching was contested in the past, largely out of professional prejudice, I doubt if anyone is in disagreement now. The method that Churchill taught in shotgun shooting is currently accepted, with only fine variations, in every coaching school.

English Shotguns and Rifles by J. N. George

Unlike Hugh Pollard, a close friend, I never met John Nigel George who was killed in the war in 1942. His book on English guns, particularly shotguns, is in my judgement one of the most thoughtful that I have read. He has courage in his opinions, and it is hard to argue with him. This book has a place in a shotgunner's collection. If he had lived he might well have taken Hugh Pollard's place in sporting literature.

The Modern Shotgun by Gerald Burrard

This three-volume work—the Gun, the Cartridge, the Gun and the Cartridge—already appears on many gunroom bookshelves. A thorough endeavour, I doubt if anybody has had the determination to read the whole of it.

Major Burrard was a veteran artillery officer in World War I. When he wrote his work on the modern shotgun he was a fussy old gentleman who did not know much about what was worth reading. His book is remarkable in that, out of a personal feud, he did not include Robert Churchill as one of the gunmakers of London in his time.

Record Bags and Shooting Records by Hugh S. Gladstone (1922)

This is a 'must' for any shooting library and I have unhesitatingly poached on it in this book. Gladstone, with a quiet patience for information, collected over the years remarkable details of the great bags and the odd shots of Victorian and Edwardian times. If you have a copy in your library you will wish to refer to it again and again.

The Big Shots, Edwardian Shooting Parties, by Jonathan Garnier Ruffer

For pleasure there is no better recent work. I have been reluctant to write at greater length on the subject here because Ruffer has written so wittily and wisely on that world which has passed by with the exit of the majority of European royalty. Not one shotgun fanatic had a clue that, within a few years, they would all be swept away. This work should be on the shelf.

The Language of Sport by C. E. Hare

A collector's guide, not in wide circulation, which will resolve all manner of arguments in the gunroom. It gives the precise traditional words, in all matters of the chase, which have been cherished over the centuries. For example it is wrong to talk of a brace of pheasants— they are a pair—and partridges are only correctly described on the game list as 'birds', although you may speak of a brace. The collective words are fascinating—a wisp of snipe, a raft of duck, an exaltation of larks, a charm of gold finches. It is a treasure to have on the shelf.

The Complete Wildfowler by Stanley Duncan and Guy Thorne

This is unquestionably the most definitive book on its subject. Stanley Duncan wrote the original work when wildfowling did not enjoy the popularity it does today. Updated, it is the Bible for wildfowling enthusiasts. But do not take your 'best gun' on dawn patrols in the saltings.

Dogs: Their History and Development by Edward C. Ash

Among the many excellent books which have been written about dogs this is the prototype. In two lavishly illustrated volumes it traces the history of all the breeds from their beginnings which, in Kennel Club terms, traces surprisingly little before the middle of the past century. Of the breeds of dogs it is perhaps not surprising that the hunters are the longest established.

Shots from a Lawyer's Gun by Nicholas Everitt and Ernest Ivens Watson

This is a fairly rare book, published by Gilbertson & Page in 1927. It is well worth having because I know no other which tackles the complex subject of the Game Laws, and the rights of the man with a gun, in such detail. So many of the laws of the field hark back to the Norman conquest. Enough that it is illegal to shoot a dog ranging on your land except to save the life of a pheasant in its mouth. If you kill a bird which falls over your neighbour's boundary, you are entitled to pick it up if it carries not more than 'a deer's leap' into the other man's land. 'A deer's leap' is one of those elastic terms which may be liberally interpreted and, if the matter comes to court, one out of which the lawyers, at any rate, may be depended upon to make themselves a handsome profit.

I am reluctant to dismiss the *Fur and Feather* series on game, published early in this century. I thought to include *The Encyclopaedia of Sport*, in two volumes, first published in 1897. In our own time, *The King in his Country*, a monograph of George VI, a splendid shot like so many of the royal family, is memorable. Eric Parker, formerly editor of '*The Field*', 'B.B.', Edward Arnold, Geoffrey Dawson and Noel Sedgwick, have all written books which will still be read by future generations.

I began this chapter suggesting that I was only recommending a skeleton shelf to begin a shooting library. I must resist the temptation to tell the reader how to enlarge his collection.

'*Nothing is certain in Law except the expense.*'

NICHOLAS EVERITT

'*The right of killing wild birds and other animals is annexed to the soil. There is, in law, no property in such things whilst alive and free. They belong to no one until they are dead or captured, and herein they differ from domesticated fowls and other animals. Although no one can justify killing a bird, a hare, or a rabbit, on or over another's land, still, at common law apart from statute, to do so was not a punishable offence. The offender might be sued at law for more or less nominal damages for the trespass, but that was in no way a deterrent to the ordinary poacher who, of course, had nothing to loose, if sued. In consequence, therefore, various Acts were from time to time passed creating new criminal offences in relation to the pursuit and taking of game.*'

SHOTS FROM A LAWYER'S GUN

APPENDICES

Appendices are normally no more than irrelevant attachments to the subject of a book. In the case of the shotgun this section has more importance than normal. In the United Kingdom in recent years the law has increasingly intervened to step up controls over the ownership of guns.

It has been suggested that the ready availability of firearms spawns crime. This is a disputable point. Criminals do not resort to fine arms, all of them carefully numbered and recorded by their makers, for their malefactions. There is overwhelming evidence that weapons used lawlessly are almost invariably cheap foreign arms imported illegally into the country. Surprisingly a high proportion of the 'exhibits' in court cases are found to have mechanical faults (very often a sticky trigger pull). Nevertheless our legislators in their urban wisdom have taken a different view.

Here is the law in the UK as it stands at the time of the publication of this work (1981). It is admonitory to point out that it may be altered in subsequent years:

Gun and Game Licences

You may not acquire a shotgun without applying for the grant of a *Shotgun Certificate* from the police. The fee is currently £12 on issue for a period of three years, £8 on renewal for a further three years. With a licence there is no limit on the number of shotguns you own. Nobody under the age of seventeen can purchase or hire any shotgun or ammunition. He may shoot; but only under the supervision of an adult.

When you apply for a Shotgun Certificate you are required, to state whether you suffer from any mental disorder, and your application must be countersigned like a passport by a senior citizen.

If you are shooting game, which excludes plebian quarry like rabbits, hares, pigeons and wildfowl, but includes the nobility of pheasants, partridges and grouse you need a *Game Licence*, which can be obtained at any Post Office, price £6 for the season. I have never been asked to produce my Game Licence in my life. The enactment was designed not as a firearms' precaution, but rather as an extra deterrent to poachers. Its usefulness remains questionable.

Protection of Birds

The basic principle of the Protection of Birds Acts, 1954–1967, is that all wild birds in Britain, including their nests and eggs, are protected by law. The Royal Society for the Protection of Birds eagerly prosecutes any offence which is brought to their attention. The exceptions are game birds, most of the wildfowl in their season and certain pest birds such as the crow family, wood pigeons, jays and magpies. The population of game birds is conserved by their keepers. Wildfowl are increasingly hand-reared to keep up their numbers.

The control is a salutory one. The needless killing of song birds and the raiding of their nests, which still persist mainly in the Latin countries of Europe, have almost ended. The consequences, not entirely unrelated to the widespread provision of bird tables in private gardens, have enriched our countryside.

Game Seasons

The seasons for killing game vary widely throughout Europe and America. It is always important to check the date appointed by the parochial authorities. In Britain this is the law which has remained unchanged up to the present time (1981):

Kind of Game	England and Wales		Scotland		Ireland	
	Begins	Ends	Begins	Ends	Begins	Ends
Grouse or moor fowl	Aug 12	Dec. 10	Aug. 12	Dec. 10	Aug. 12	Dec 10
Black game or heath fowl	Aug 20	Dec 10	Aug 20	Dec 10	Aug 20	Dec 10
Ptarmigan	—	—	Aug 12	Dec 10	—	—
Partridge	Sept 1	Feb 1	Sept 1	Feb 1	Sept 1	Feb 1
Pheasant	Oct 1	Feb 1	Oct 1	Feb 1	Oct 1	Feb 1
Quail	As wild birds		As wild birds		Sept 20	Jan 10
Landrail	,,	,,	,,	,,	Sept 20	Jan 10
Hare	No close season		No close season		Apr 20	Aug 12
Male fallow deer	,,	,,	,,	,,	June 10	Sept 29
Other male deer	,,	,,	,,	,,	June 10	Dec 31
Wildfowl or other birds not game	Aug 1	Mar 1	Aug 1	Mar 1	Aug 1	Mar 1

Bores of Shotguns

87 per cent of cartridges are now fired through 12-bore guns. The figure is distorted to some extent because it includes cartridges used for clay pigeon shooting. In game shooting the 16- and 20-bore still have a place. The other bores are now largely of interest to collectors. But, for the record, these are the sizes which throughout the century have found favour:

Description	Approximate Shot Charge oz	Approximate Weight of Gun lbs
4-bore 4in	3—4	$14\frac{1}{2}$—$18\frac{1}{2}$
8-bore $3\frac{1}{4}$in	2—$2\frac{1}{2}$	$10\frac{1}{2}$—$12\frac{1}{2}$
10-bore $2\frac{7}{8}$in	$1\frac{7}{16}$—$1\frac{5}{8}$	8—9
10-bore $2\frac{5}{8}$in	$1\frac{1}{4}$—$1\frac{3}{8}$	$7\frac{1}{2}$—8
12-bore 3in*	$1\frac{3}{8}$—$1\frac{1}{2}$	$7\frac{3}{4}$—$8\frac{1}{2}$
12-bore $2\frac{3}{4}$in*	$1\frac{1}{4}$	$7\frac{1}{2}$—$7\frac{3}{4}$
12-bore $2\frac{1}{2}$in*	1—$1\frac{1}{8}$	$6\frac{1}{2}$
16-bore $2\frac{3}{4}$in*	1—$1\frac{1}{16}$	$6\frac{1}{2}$—7
16-bore $2\frac{1}{2}$in	$\frac{7}{8}$—$\frac{15}{16}$	$5\frac{3}{4}$—6
20-bore $2\frac{3}{4}$in	$\frac{7}{8}$—$\frac{15}{16}$	$5\frac{3}{4}$—6
20-bore $2\frac{1}{2}$in	$\frac{3}{4}$—$\frac{13}{16}$	$5\frac{1}{2}$
24-bore $2\frac{1}{2}$in	$\frac{11}{16}$	5
28-bore $2\frac{1}{2}$in	$\frac{5}{8}$	$4\frac{3}{4}$
32-bore $2\frac{1}{2}$in	$\frac{1}{2}$	4
.410-bore $2\frac{1}{2}$in	$\frac{7}{16}$	$3\frac{3}{4}$

*Guns with 25in barrels are built approximately 8oz lighter.

★　★　★　★

4-bore .950in 8-bore .847in 12-bore .740in 16-bore .673in 20-bore .625in 28-bore .558in .410-bore .410in	Minimum diameter of card wadding.	The actual barrel diameter of a 12-bore gun is, as a rule, .729in, decreasing at the choke according to the degree of choke left in the barrel by the maker.

Shot Details

It is not so important now to consider different shot sizes which occasioned so much interest in the past, but the table which follows gives the essential information. Mould shot, from LG to B, is still cast. The rest is drop-shot from the tower:

Designation	Pellets per oz	Weight per Pellet (Grains)	Diameter (Inches)
LG	5	87.50	.388
MG	7	62.50	.347
SG	8	54.70	.332
Special SG	11	39.80	.298
SSG	15	29.17	.269
SSSG	20	21.89	.245
SSSSG	25	17.50	.227
SSSSSG	30	14.58	.214
AAA	35	12.50	.203
AA	40	10.94	.194
A	50	8.75	.180
BBB	60	7.29	.170
BB	70	6.25	.161
B	80	5.47	.154
1	100	4.38	.143
2	120	3.65	.135
3	140	3.12	.128
4	170	2.57	.120
5	220	1.99	.110
5½	240	1.82	.107
6	270	1.62	.102
6½	300	1.46	.099
7	340	1.29	.095
8	450	0.97	.087
9	580	0.75	.080
10	850	0.51	.070

Speed of Game Birds

The subject, so often discussed in gunrooms, has never been fully resolved. It never will be because wind and weather make such an important difference to flight. The contours of the ground are another factor. But, with reservations, it may be concluded that the following table, in average conditions, is acceptable:

	Miles per Hour
Pheasants in full flight move at approximately	38—40
Partridges ,, ,, ,, ,,	32—36
Grouse ,, ,, ,, ,,	40—50
Wild duck ,, ,, ,, ,,	40—45
Teal ,, ,, ,, ,,	60—65
Geese ,, ,, ,, ,,	50—55

Pellets in Game Charges

oz of Shot	Size of Shot			
	4	5	6	7
$1\frac{1}{2}$	255	330	408	510
$1\frac{7}{16}$	244	316	391	489
$1\frac{3}{8}$	234	303	374	468
$1\frac{5}{16}$	223	289	357	446
$1\frac{1}{4}$	213	275	340	425
$1\frac{3}{16}$	202	261	323	404
$1\frac{1}{8}$	191	248	306	383
$1\frac{1}{16}$	181	234	289	361
1	170	220	272	340
$\frac{15}{16}$	159	206	255	319
$\frac{7}{8}$	149	193	238	298
$\frac{13}{16}$	138	179	221	276
$\frac{3}{4}$	128	165	204	255
$\frac{11}{16}$	117	151	187	234
$\frac{5}{8}$	106	138	170	212
$\frac{9}{16}$	96	124	153	191
$\frac{1}{2}$	85	110	136	170

★　★　★　★

True Cylinder (=40 per cent) Patterns

oz of Shot	Pellets in 30in circle at 40 YARDS for different SIZES of Shot			
	4	5	6	7
$1\frac{1}{2}$	102	132	163	204
$1\frac{3}{8}$	94	121	150	187
$1\frac{1}{4}$	85	110	136	170
$1\frac{1}{8}$	76	99	122	153
$1\frac{1}{16}$	72	94	116	144
1	68	88	109	136
$\frac{7}{8}$	60	77	95	119
$\frac{3}{4}$	51	66	82	102
$\frac{11}{16}$	47	60	75	94
$\frac{5}{8}$	42	55	68	85
$\frac{9}{16}$	38	50	61	76
$\frac{1}{2}$	34	44	54	68

Improved Cylinder (= 50 per cent) Patterns

oz of Shot	Pellets in 30in circle at 40 YARDS for different SIZES of Shot			
	4	5	6	7
$1\frac{1}{2}$	128	165	204	255
$1\frac{7}{16}$	122	158	196	245
$1\frac{3}{8}$	117	152	187	234
$1\frac{5}{16}$	111	145	179	223
$1\frac{1}{4}$	107	138	170	213
$1\frac{3}{16}$	101	131	162	202
$1\frac{1}{8}$	96	124	153	192
$1\frac{1}{16}$	91	117	145	181
1	85	110	136	170
$\frac{15}{16}$	80	103	128	160
$\frac{7}{8}$	75	97	119	149
$\frac{13}{16}$	69	90	111	138
$\frac{3}{4}$	64	83	102	128
$\frac{11}{16}$	59	76	94	117
$\frac{5}{8}$	53	69	85	106
$\frac{9}{16}$	48	62	77	96
$\frac{1}{2}$	43	55	68	85

★ ★ ★ ★

Half Choke (= 60 per cent) Patterns

oz of Shot	Pellets in 30in circle at 40 YARDS for different SIZES of Shot			
	4	5	6	7
$1\frac{1}{2}$	153	198	244	306
$1\frac{7}{16}$	146	190	235	293
$1\frac{3}{8}$	140	182	224	280
$1\frac{5}{16}$	134	174	214	267
$1\frac{1}{4}$	128	165	204	255
$1\frac{3}{16}$	121	157	194	242
$1\frac{1}{8}$	115	148	148	230
$1\frac{1}{16}$	109	140	173	217
1	102	132	163	204
$\frac{15}{16}$	95	125	153	191
$\frac{7}{8}$	89	116	143	179
$\frac{13}{16}$	83	108	133	166
$\frac{3}{4}$	77	99	122	153
$\frac{11}{16}$	70	91	112	140
$\frac{5}{8}$	64	82	102	127
$\frac{9}{16}$	58	74	92	115
$\frac{1}{2}$	51	66	81	102

Full Choke (== 70 per cent) Patterns

oz of Shot	Pellets in 30in circle at 40 Yards for different Sizes of Shot			
	4	5	6	7
$1\frac{1}{2}$	178	231	285	357
$1\frac{7}{16}$	170	221	274	342
$1\frac{3}{8}$	163	212	261	328
$1\frac{5}{16}$	156	202	249	312
$1\frac{1}{4}$	149	192	238	298
$1\frac{3}{16}$	142	183	226	283
$1\frac{1}{8}$	134	174	214	268
$1\frac{1}{16}$	127	164	202	253
1	119	154	190	238
$\frac{15}{16}$	112	144	179	223
$\frac{7}{8}$	105	135	167	209
$\frac{13}{16}$	97	125	155	194
$\frac{3}{4}$	90	115	143	179
$\frac{11}{16}$	82	106	131	163
$\frac{5}{8}$	75	97	119	148
$\frac{9}{16}$	67	86	107	134
$\frac{1}{2}$	59	77	95	119

Patterns and Penetration

Firing a load of $1\frac{1}{16}$oz of shot for pattern at a range of 40yd, the following numbers of pellets should be within the 30in circle. 'Cartwheels' or patterns with a blank centre are ignored.

	No 5 Shot	No 6 Shot
True cylinder (40 per cent)	94	116
Improved cylinder (50 per cent)	117	145
Half choke (60 per cent)	140	173
Full choke (70 per cent)	164	202

Penetration is best roughly tested by comparison of a known efficient cartridge with those under test. Shots fired at cheap periodicals or books under the same conditions afford a ready means of comparison, as the depth of penetration can be read off in pages. The penetration or indentation of thin, flat cigarette tins is also a useful indication. If shot passes through both sides at 25yd, all is well.

Length of 12-Bore Cases

The standard pasteboard 12-bore game cartridge is nominally $2\frac{1}{2}$in long (actually $2\frac{9}{16}$in). The American standard case is slightly longer—$2\frac{5}{8}$in—and guns built for overseas use should be chambered to take the long case.

Pigeon guns take a $2\frac{3}{4}$in case, and wild fowl guns are usually chambered for the 3in case. Special guns for short 2in cases should be avoided.

There is no objection to the use of short cases in guns with long chambers although pattern may be adversely affected, *but long cases must never be used in chambers too short for them.* There is inevitably an undue rise in pressure and consequent recoil, and there is serious danger of a burst or damaged gun. The mere fact that a longer unfired cartridge will fit the chamber must be ignored, for though it may fit it when unfired, the unrolling of the turnover on firing over-fills the chambers and creates a narrowing at the cone where the chamber leads into the barrel.

Small Bore Cases
The 2½in case is standard for all small bores, but 2¾in cases for 16- and 20-bores are in occasional use. The .410 now takes the 2½in case or 'Four-long' as standard, but in the past was made for a short 2in case. Long cases must not be used in the short-chambered guns.

Standard Cartridge Loads
The full 12-bore load is 1⅛oz of shot, but the modern tendency to light guns has meant a general trend towards charges of 1 1/16 or 1oz. In practice, the lighter load is just as efficient and gives a more regular pattern.

Spread of Shot
The following table gives the diameter of the spread of shot with normal loads to the nearest *inch*.

DISTANCES IN YARDS

Boring	5 in	10 in	15 in	20 in	25 in	30 in	35 in	40 in
True cylinder	8¾	19	26	32	38	44	51	57
One-eighth choke	7¾	17	23	29	35	41	47	54
Quarter choke	6¾	15	20	26	32	38	44	51
Half choke	5¾	12	16	20	26	32	38	46
Three-quarter choke	5⅛	10½	14	18	23½	29	35	43
Full choke	4½	9	12	16	21	26	32	40

ACKNOWLEDGEMENTS

It is customary to make acknowledgements at the beginning of a book. It seems to me that, if the book was worth reading, it is more appropriate to list them at the end.

By gracious permission of Her Majesty the Queen, I was permitted to visit her private house at Sandringham in Norfolk and to photograph stands on the estate and some of the remarkable collection of weapons there (dust jacket and pages 75, 76, 77, 140, 141, 154, 157, 215). Apart from a wildfowling piece which I have illustrated, none of George VI's guns are in the collection. I am told that Prince Charles, for whom their fit is ideal, uses them himself. Traditionally, most of the royal guns are made by Purdey's, whose name ornaments many pages in the book. Another great name in London gunmaking, Messrs Holland & Holland, is recorded on pages 34, 66, 74, 166 and 191.

I acknowledge photographs by my friend the master photographer John Gay (pages 32, 33, 34, 39, 51, 52, 74, 75, 76, 77, 85, 92, 145, 147, 159, 160, 161, 162, 163, 189, 207, 208); and I thank the more impersonal Radio Times Hulton Picture Library for pictures on pages 64, 65, 66, 184, 185, 187, 193, 194, 195, 196 and 198, which I largely directed in the field myself.

I must also record my thanks to the Viscount Coke of Holkham; his photographer, Alan Howard, who recorded Gainsborough's portrait of Thomas Coke; and Mr F. C. Jolly, the administrator of the estate, whose help was invaluable (pages 140, 145, 147, 155). My thanks to David Warmington, who drew all the diagrams in this book; to the Brod Gallery of London, who supplied me with the photograph of the oil painting on page 21; to Eley, the cartridge makers (page 98); to Mr. K. D. A. Keith for the painting of the West Barsham Game Cart (page 104); to Colonel C. P. Dawnay, CBE, MVO for his photographs of

233

Longparish House in Hampshire; to the Pembroke Estate for the old photograph of Lord de Grey shooting at Wilton; to the Viscount Camrose and Colonel the Hon Julian Berry for the photographs taken at Hackwood in Hampshire; to the Lord Iliffe for the photographs at Yattendon; to the Tryon Gallery for the reproductions of various sporting prints throughout the book; to Mr Jonathan Garnier Ruffer and Debrett's Peerage for the photograph of Sir Ralph Payne-Gallwey in his Yorkshire gunroom; to the Game Conservancy at Fordingbridge for the mounted game birds.

I trust that I have not left anyone out. So many helped me.

INDEX